Success

Assessment Papers

Non-Verbal Reasoning

age 7 – 8

Pamela Macey

paper number for quick reference

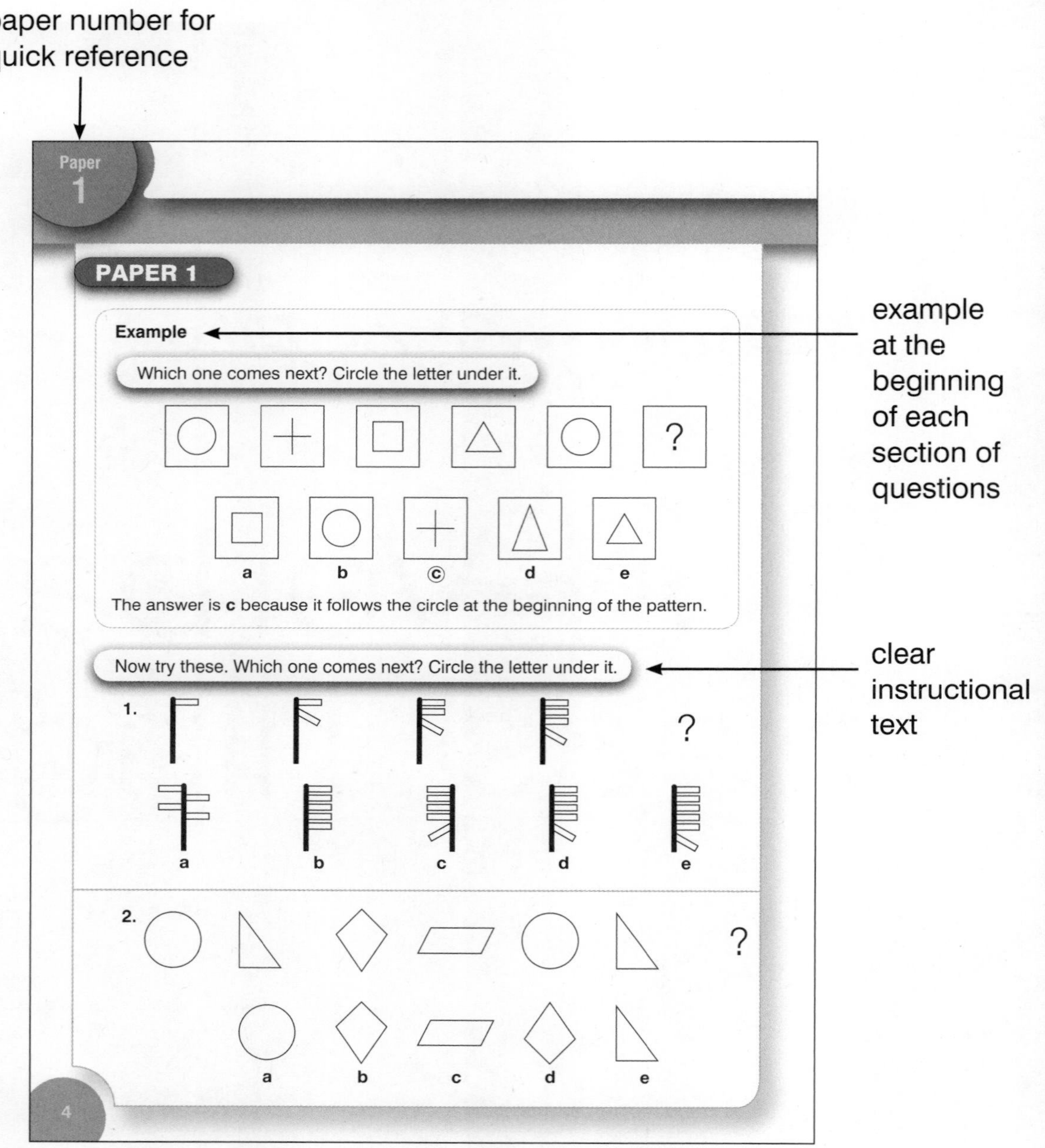
Paper
1
PAPER 1
Example
Which one comes next? Circle the letter under it.
?
a
b
c
d
e
The answer is **c** because it follows the circle at the beginning of the pattern.
Now try these. Which one comes next? Circle the letter under it.
1.
?
a
b
c
d
e
2.
?
a
b
c
d
e
4

example at the beginning of each section of questions

clear instructional text

Contents

PAPER 1	4
PAPER 2	12
PAPER 3	20
PAPER 4	28
PAPER 5	35
PAPER 6	44
PAPER 7	52
PAPER 8	60
Progress grid	68
Answer booklet	1–4

PAPER 1

Example

Which one comes next? Circle the letter under it.

a b ⓒ d e

The answer is **c** because it follows the circle at the beginning of the pattern.

Now try these. Which one comes next? Circle the letter under it.

1.

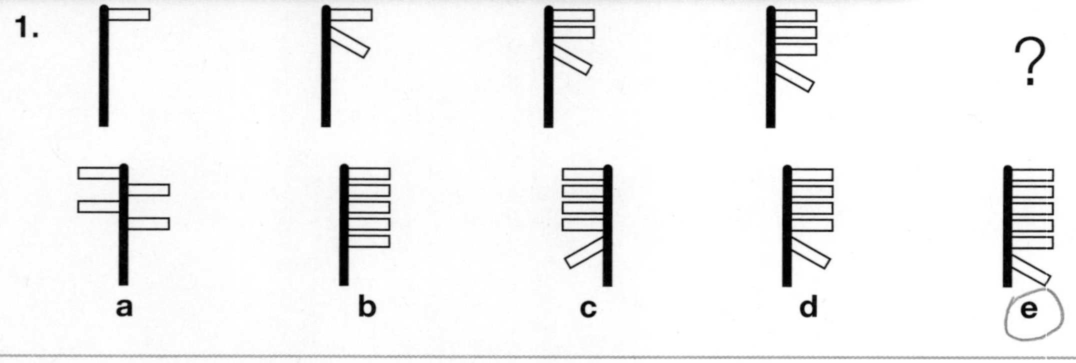

a b c d e

2.

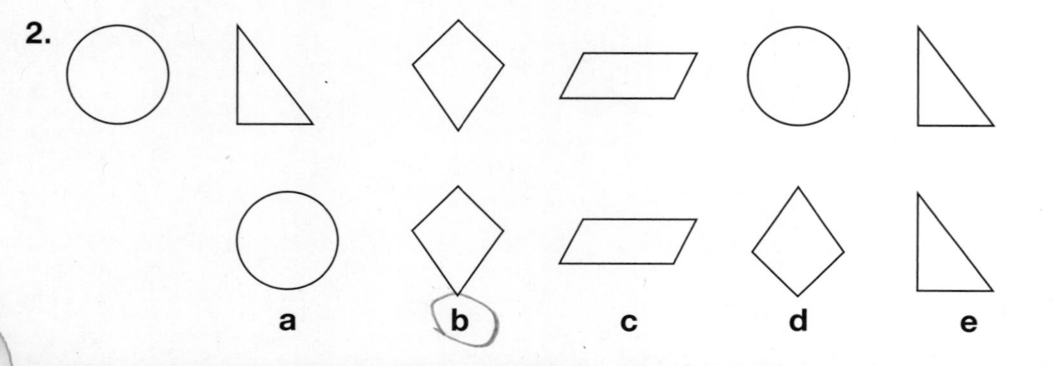

a b c d e

3. ? a b c d e

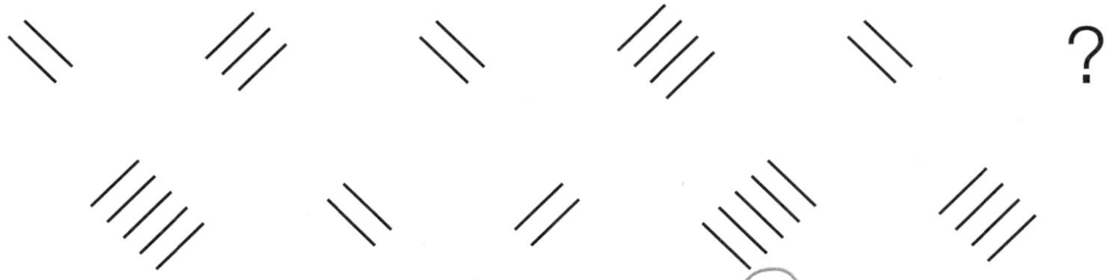

4. ? a b c d e

5. ? a b c d e

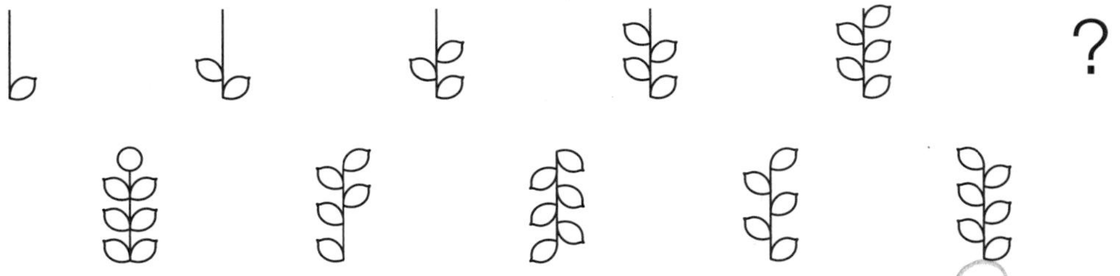

/5

Example

Which is the odd one out? Circle the letter under it.

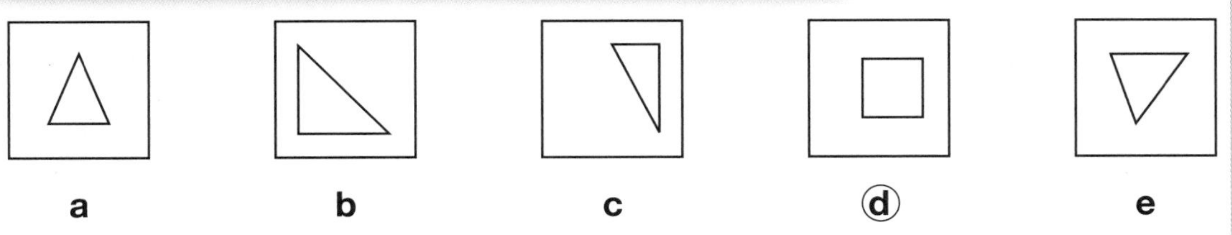

a b c ⓓ e

The answer is **d** because the shape inside the square has 4 sides. **a**, **b**, **c** and **e** are all similar because the shape inside each square has 3 sides.

Now try these. Which is the odd one out? Circle the letter under it.

6. 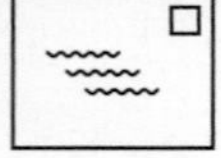  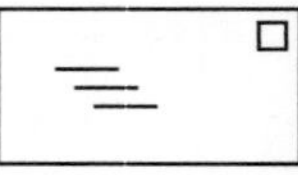

a b c d e

7. 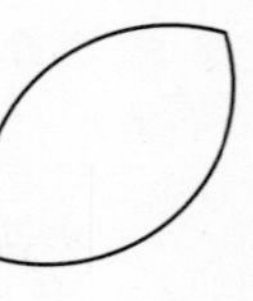   

a b c d e

8.   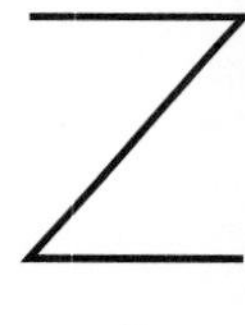

a b c d e

9.  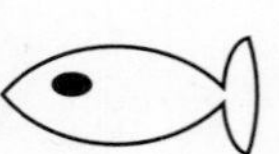 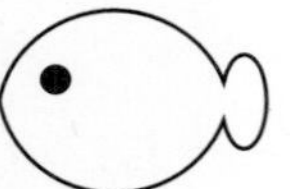 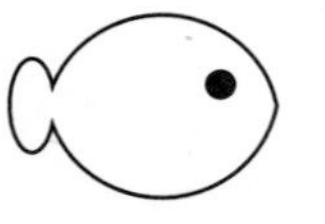 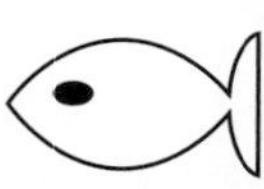

a b c d e

10. 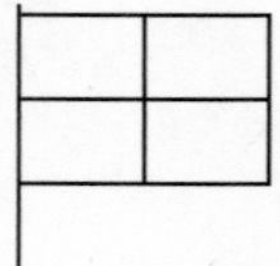 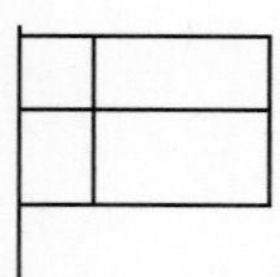 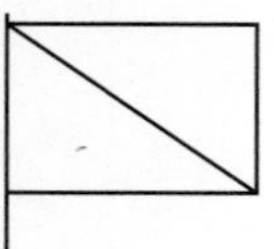 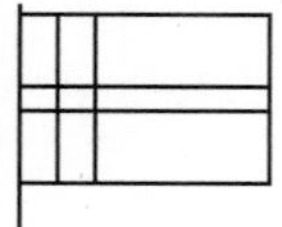 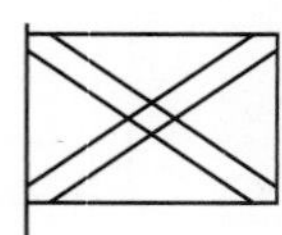

a b c d e

/5

Example

Match the missing part of the second pair in a similar way to the first pair. Circle the letter under the missing part.

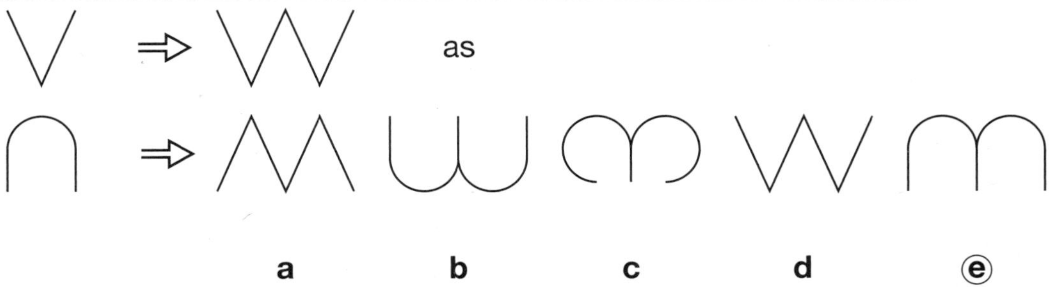

as

a b c d (e)

The answer is **e** because in this example, the answer is double the first one.

Now try these. Circle the letter under the missing part.

11.

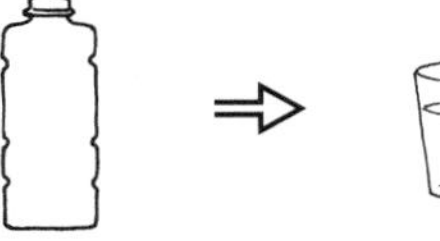

as

a b c d e

12.

 ⇒ ABC as

 ⇒ abc 123  XYZ 

a b c d e

13.  as

A ⇒ B I R V Z

a b c d e

14. 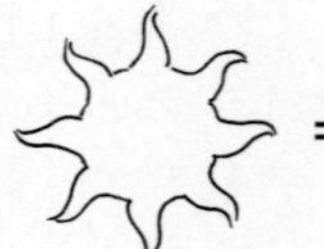 ⇒  as

 ⇒     

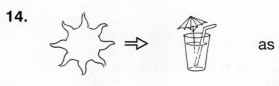

a b c d e

15.  ⇒  as

 ⇒ 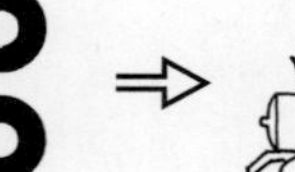      

a b c d e

/5

Example

Complete the grid by finding the missing square. Circle the letter under the square.

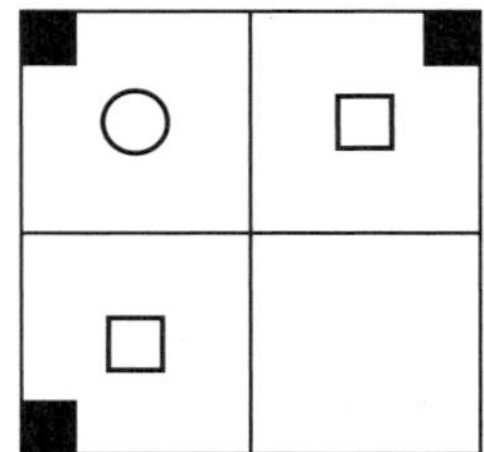

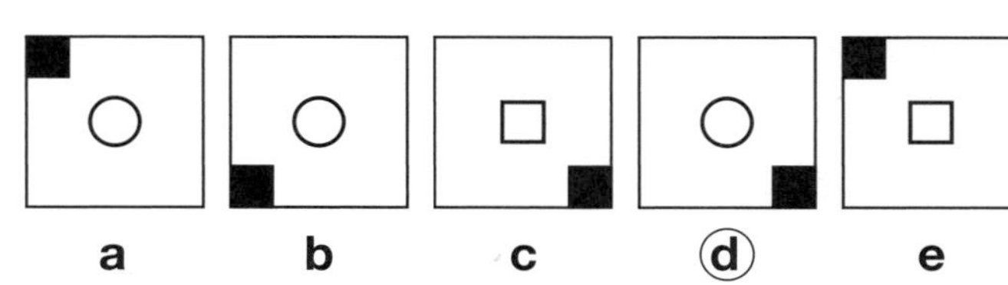

a b c (d) e

The answer is **d** because the small black squares make a pattern on the outer corners of the whole grid.

The middle of the missing part is a circle. The top of the grid is a circle and a square, so the bottom line becomes a square and then a circle.

Now try these. Circle the letter under the missing square.

16.

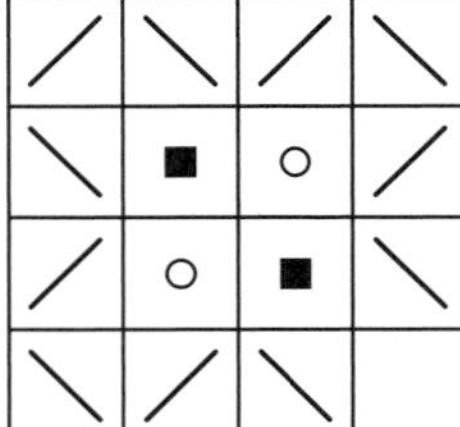

a b c d e

17.

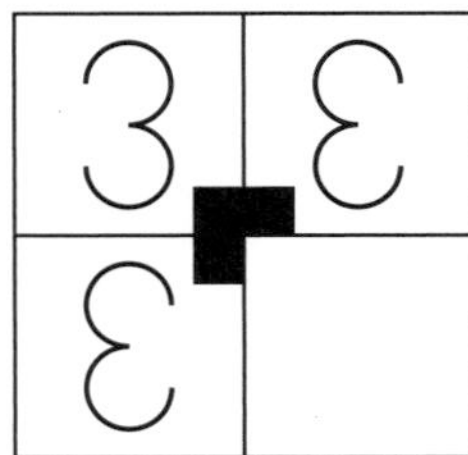

a

b

c

d

e

18.

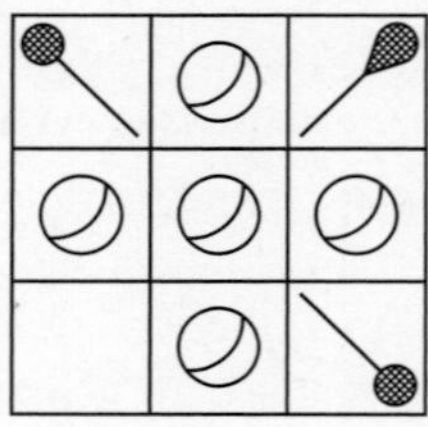

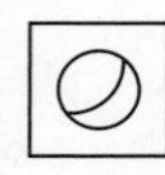    

a b c d e

19.

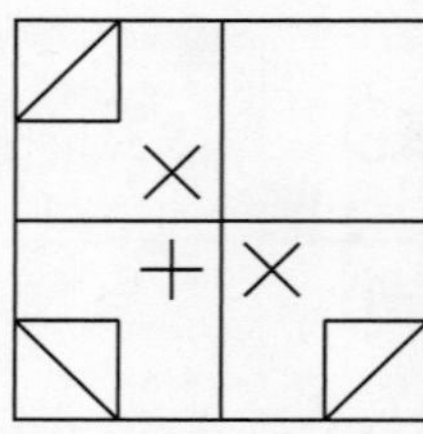

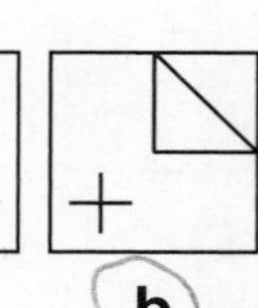 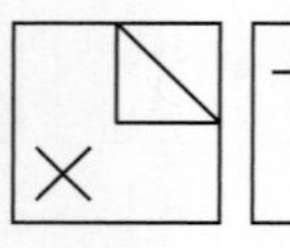 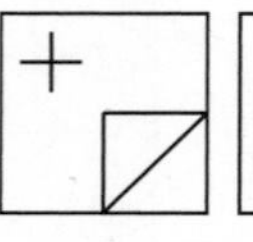 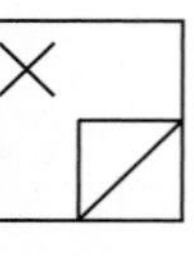

a b c d e

20.

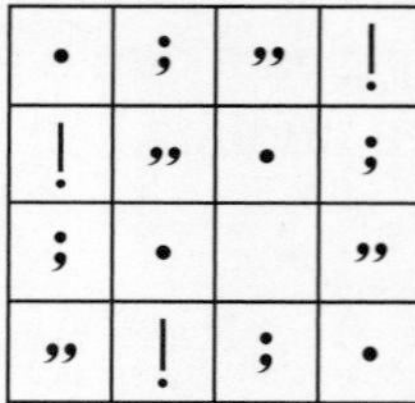

a b c d e

/5

Example

Look at the shapes and patterns. Work out the code by putting the pattern and shape together. Circle the letter under the code.

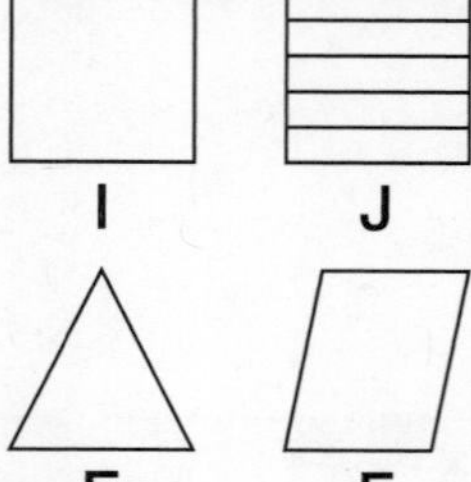

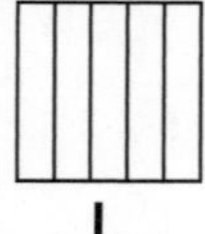

I J K L

E F G H

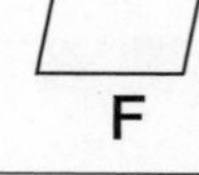

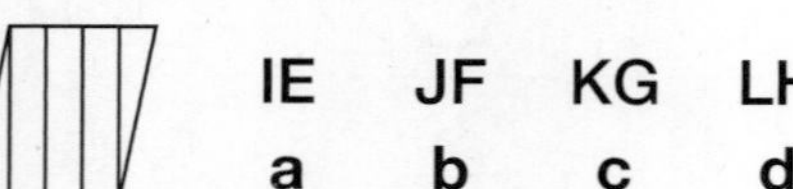

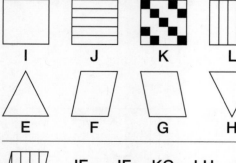

IE	JF	KG	LH	LF
a	b	c	d	(e)

The answer is **e** because the pattern is **L** and the shape is **F**, so the code is **LF**.

Now try these. Use the shapes and patterns below to answer the questions.

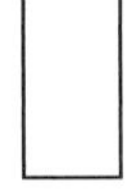		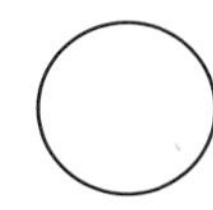	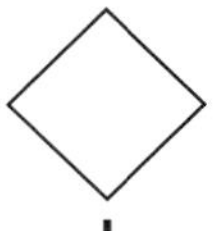		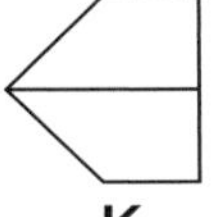	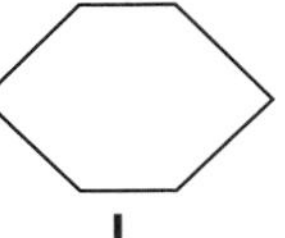	
F	G	H	I	J	K	L	M
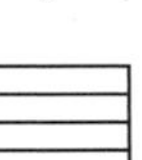					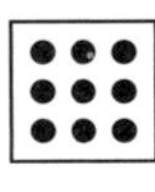	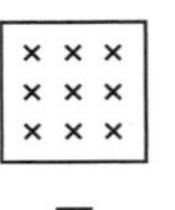	
Z	Y	X	W	V	U	T	S

21. 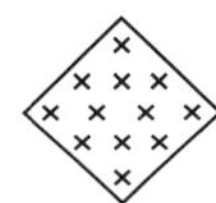

IT	JU	JT	HU	IS
a	b	c	d	e

22. 

JY	MV	MU	JV	MY
a	b	c	d	e

23. 

JY	JZ	IZ	MX	MV
a	b	c	d	e

24. 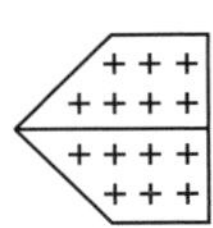

LS	KU	LT	KS	KT
a	b	c	d	e

25. 

MV	FV	FY	IY	FZ
a	b	c	d	e

/5

/25

PAPER 2

Example

Complete the grid by finding the missing square. Circle the letter under the square.

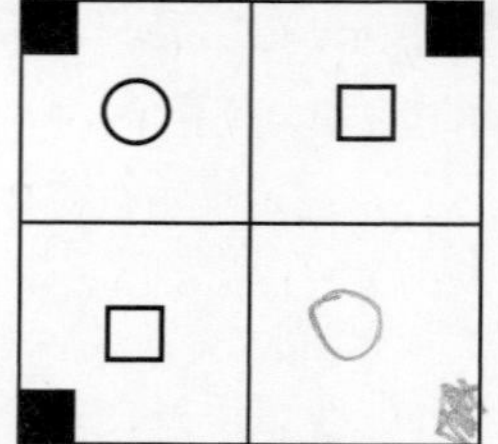

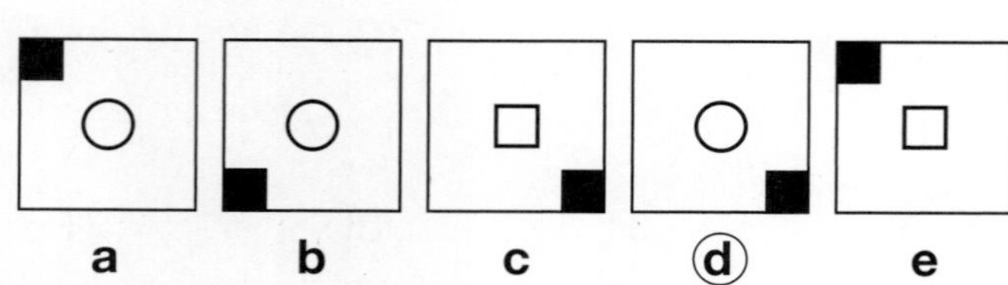

a b c d e

The answer is **d** because the small black squares make a pattern on the outer corners of the whole grid.

The middle of the missing part is a circle. The top of the grid is a circle and a square, so the bottom line becomes a square and then a circle.

Now try these. Circle the letter under the missing square.

1.

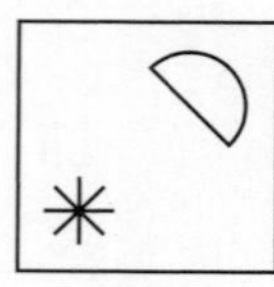

a b c d e

2.

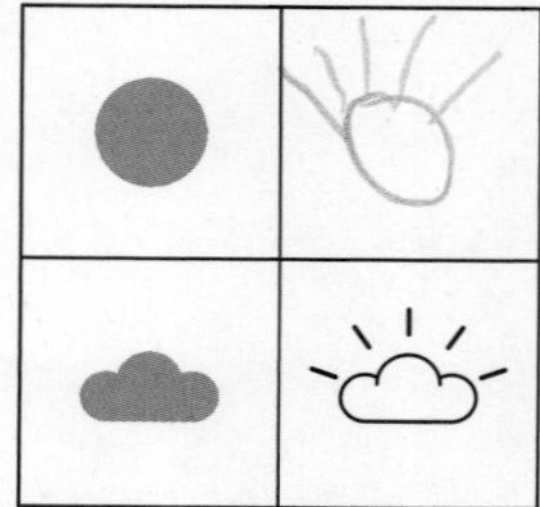

a b c d e

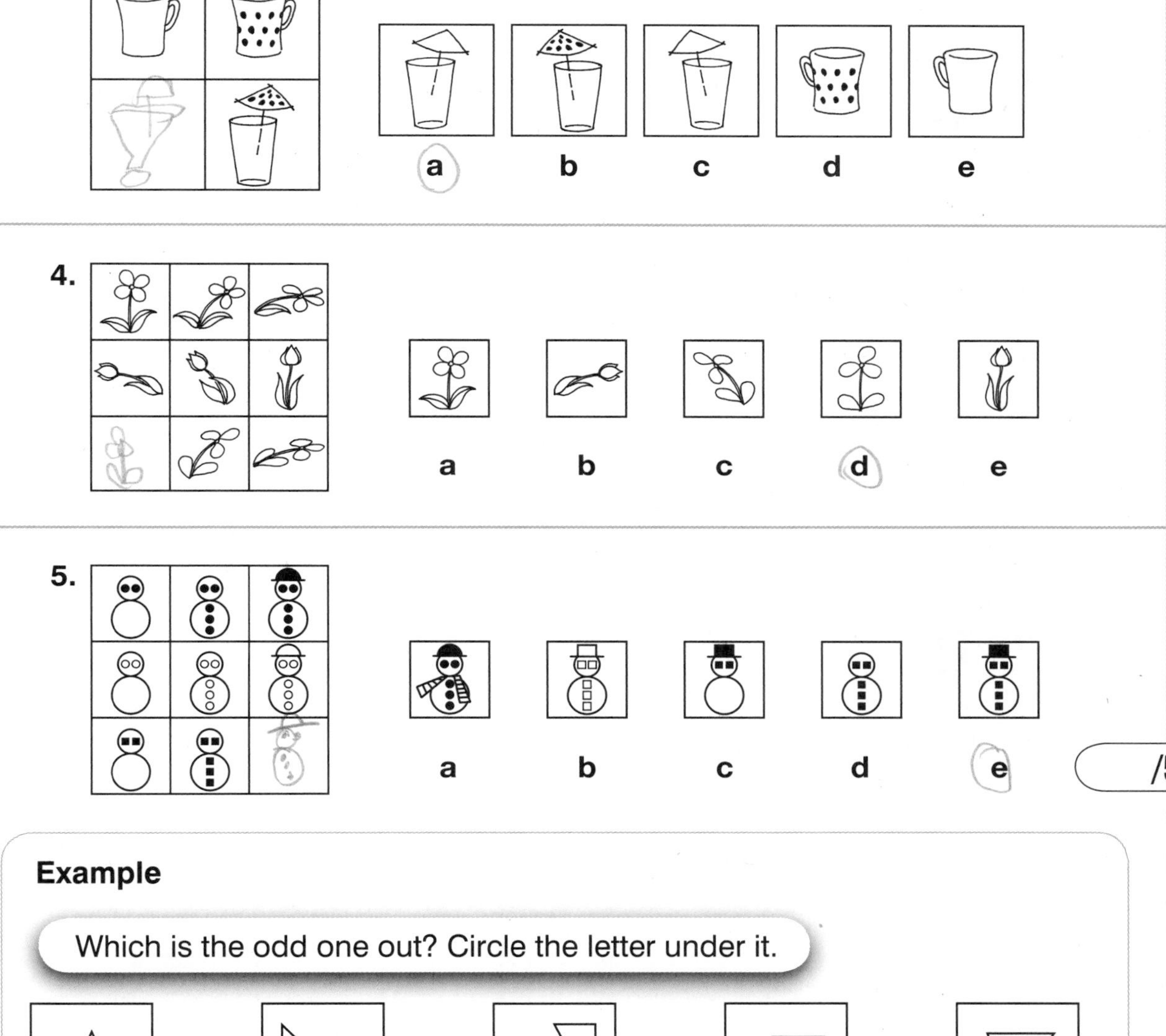

Example

Which is the odd one out? Circle the letter under it.

a b c (d) e

The answer is **d** because the shape inside the square has 4 sides. **a**, **b**, **c** and **e** are all similar because the shape inside each square has 3 sides.

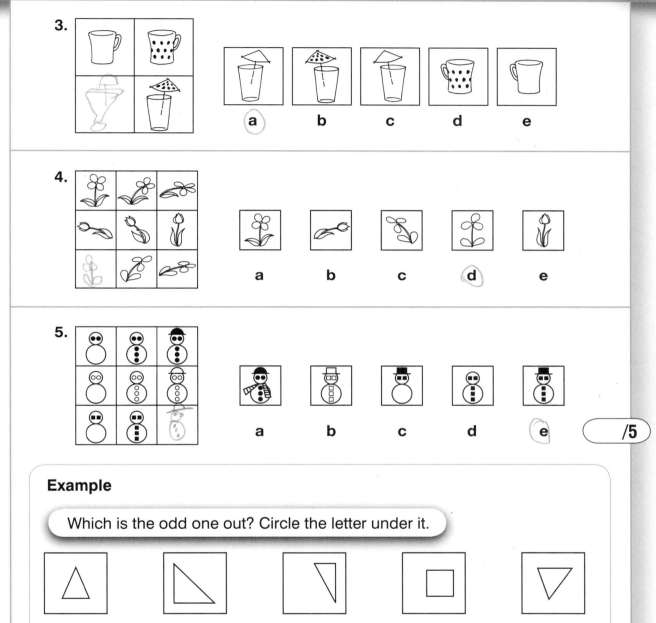

Now try these. Which is the odd one out? Circle the letter under it.

6. 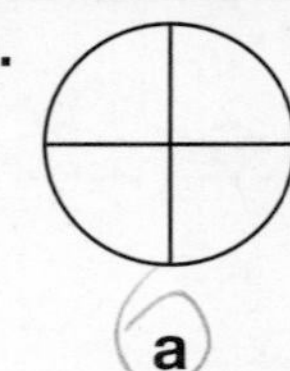 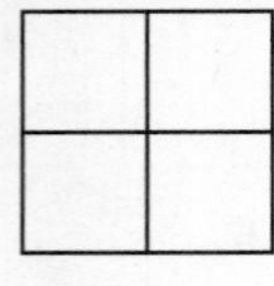 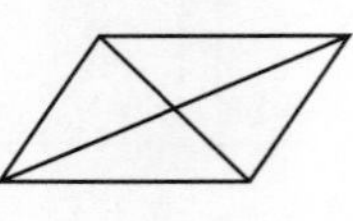 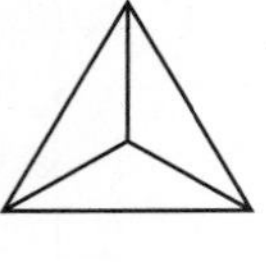 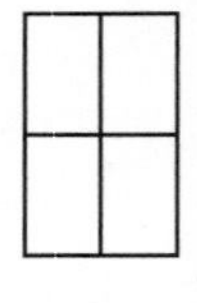

a b c d e

7.    

a b c d e

8.   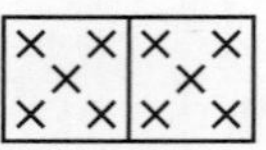 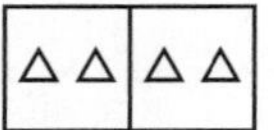 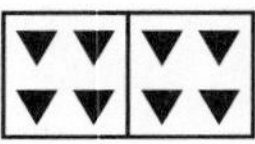

a b c d e

9. 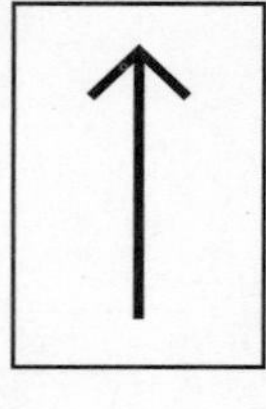    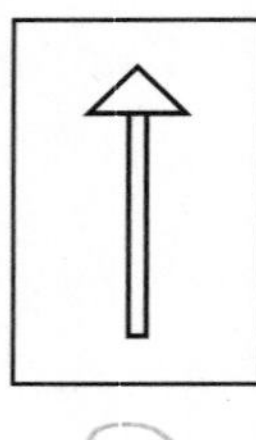

a b c d e

10. a B P Q D

a b c d e

/5

Example

Look at the shapes and patterns. Work out the code by putting the pattern and shape together. Circle the letter under the code.

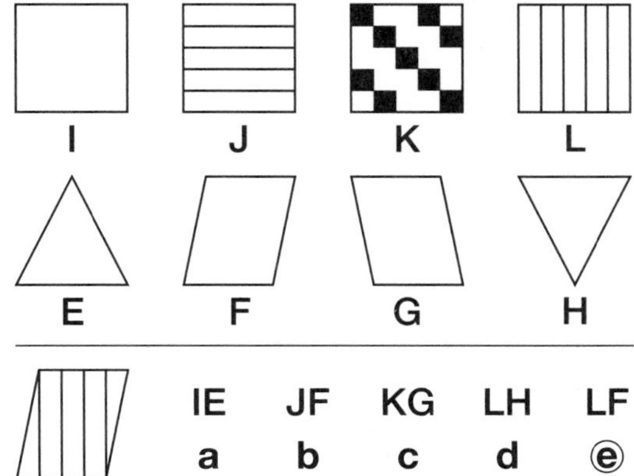

The answer is **e** because the pattern is **L** and the shape is **F**, so the code is **LF**.

Now try these. Use the shapes and patterns below to answer the questions.

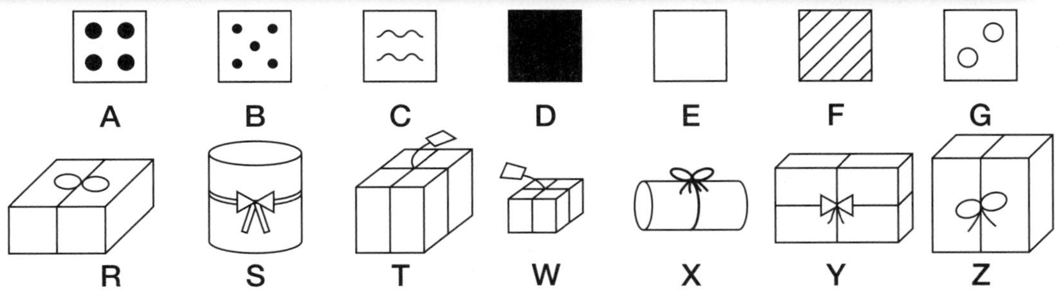

11. 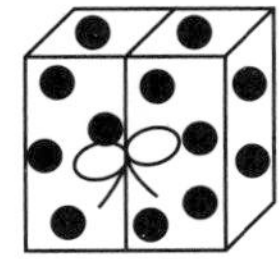

AZ	BZ	AR	BR	AT
a	b	c	d	e

12. 

DX	CS	CX	DS	CW
a	b	c	d	e

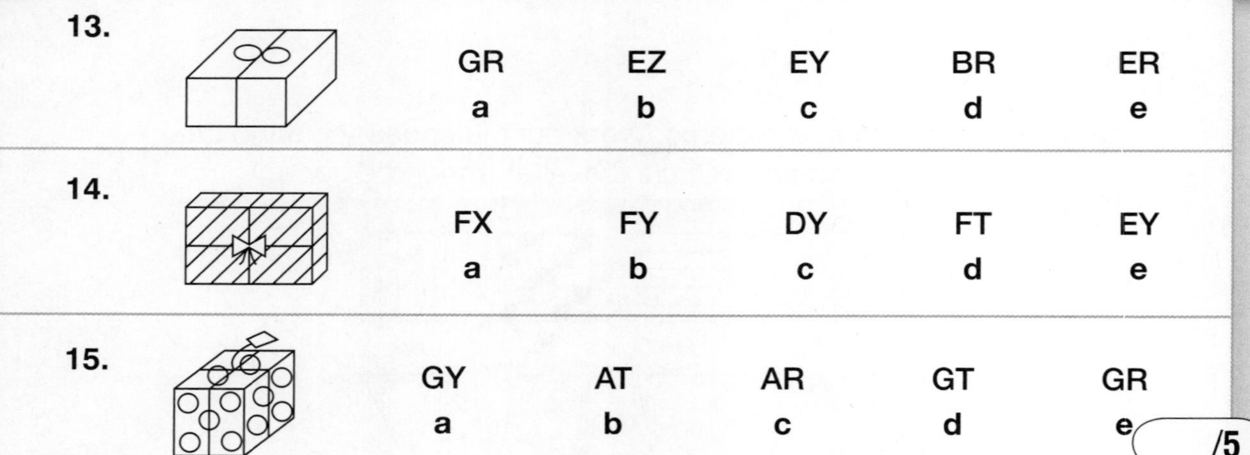

13. GR a | EZ b | EY c | BR d | ER e

14. FX a | FY b | DY c | FT d | EY e

15. GY a | AT b | AR c | GT d | GR e

/5

Example

Which one comes next? Circle the letter under it.

a b ⓒ d e

The answer is **c** because it follows the circle at the beginning of the pattern.

Now try these. Which one comes next? Circle the letter under it.

16.

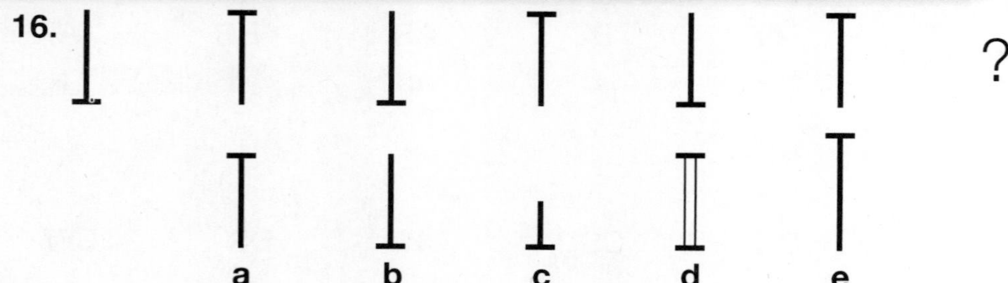

a b c d e

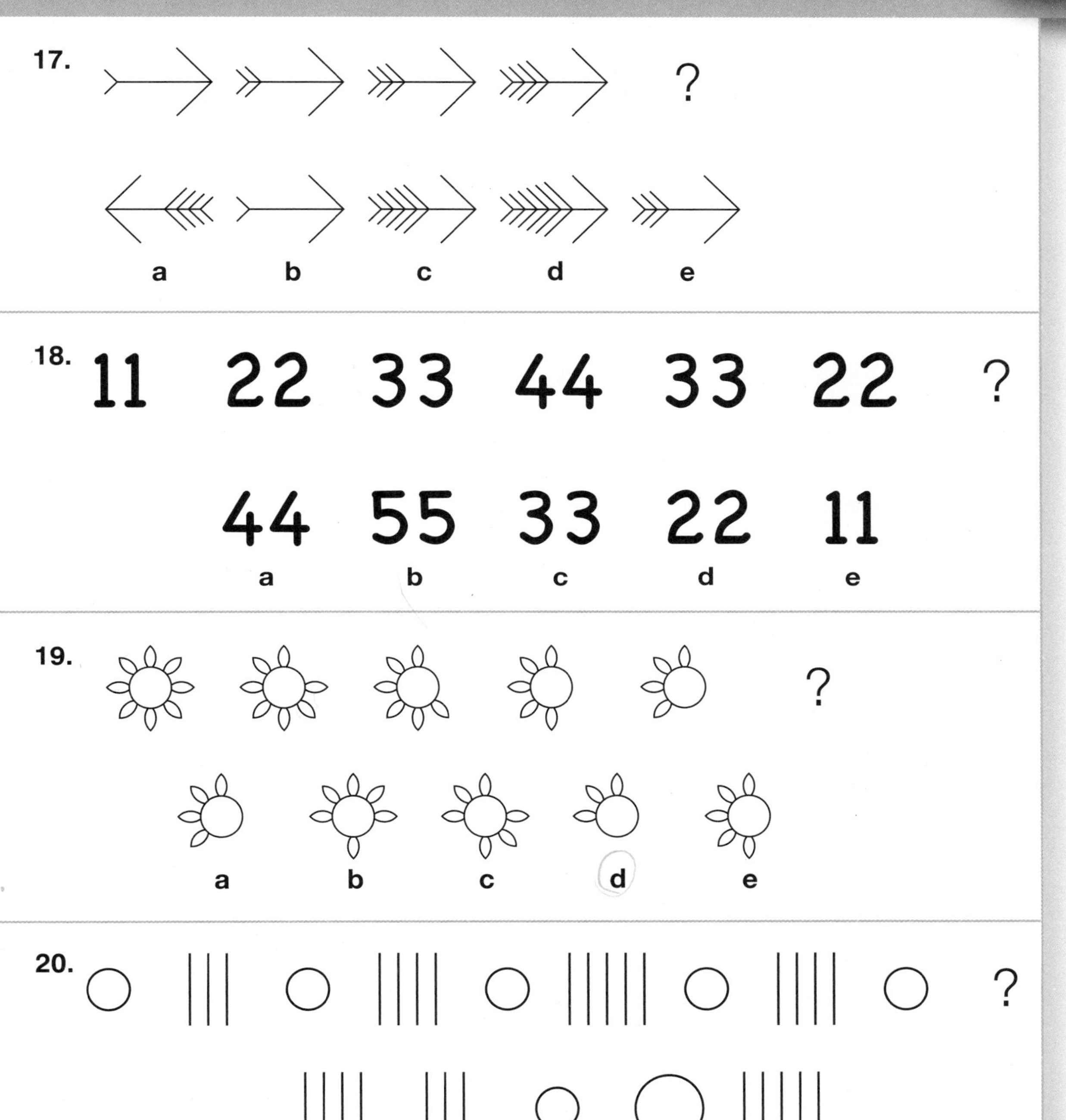
17.
?
a b c d e
18.
11 22 33 44 33 22 ?
44 55 33 22 11
a b c d e
19.
?
a b c d e
20.
?
a b c d e

/5

Example

Match the missing part of the second pair in a similar way to the first pair. Circle the letter under the missing part.

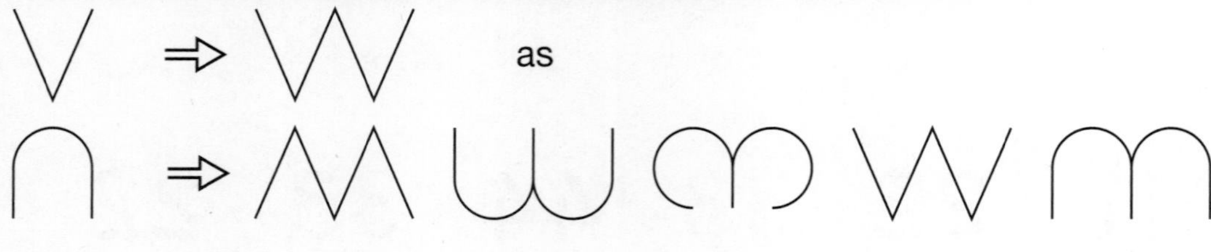

a b c d ⓔ

The answer is **e** because in this example, the answer is double the first one.

Now try these. Circle the letter under the missing part.

21.

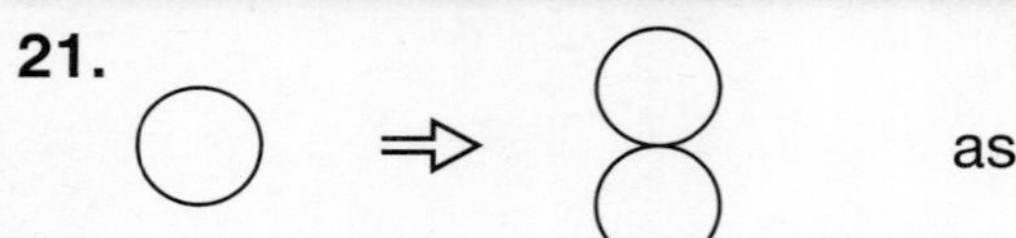

a b c d e

22.

as

a b c d e

23.  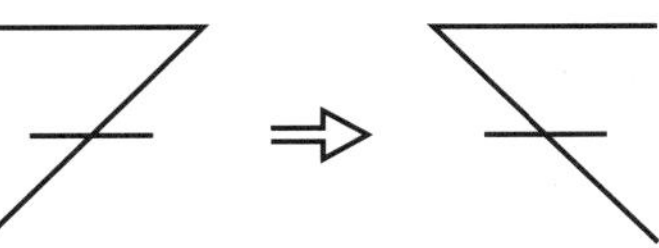 as

   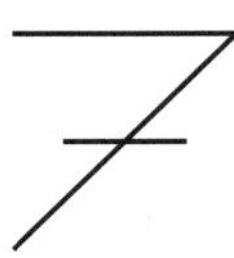  

a **b** **c** **d** **e**

24. 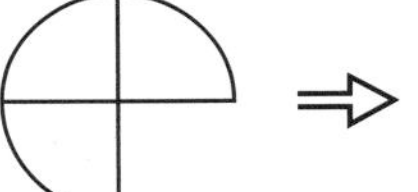 as

 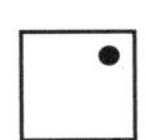

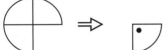

a **b** **c** **d** **e**

25. 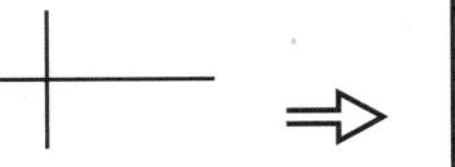 as

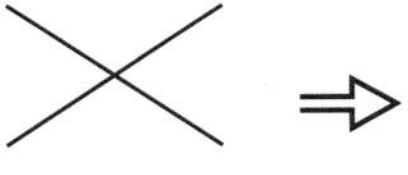 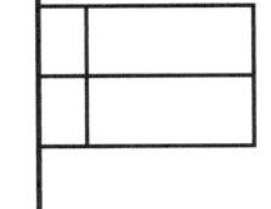 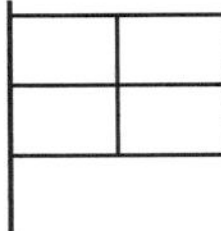 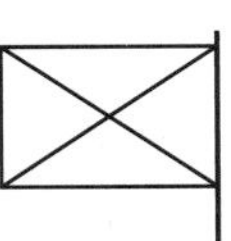 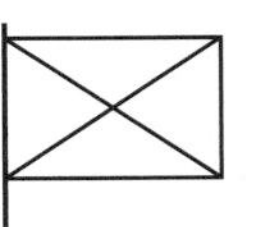 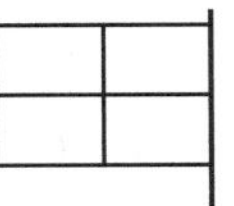

a **b** **c** **d** **e**

/5

/25

PAPER 3

Example

Which is the odd one out? Circle the letter under it.

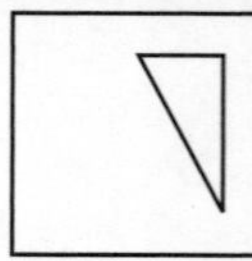

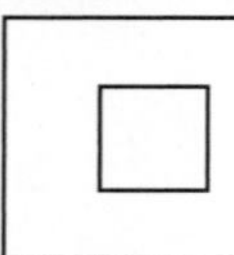

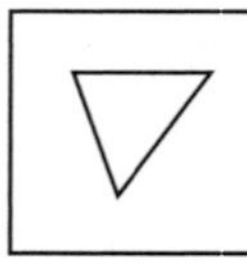

a b c (d) e

The answer is **d** because the shape inside the square has 4 sides. **a**, **b**, **c** and **e** are all similar because the shape inside each square has 3 sides.

Now try these. Which is the odd one out? Circle the letter under it.

1.

a b c d e f

2.

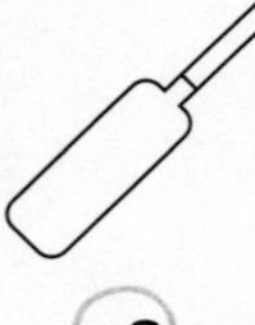

a b c d e

3.

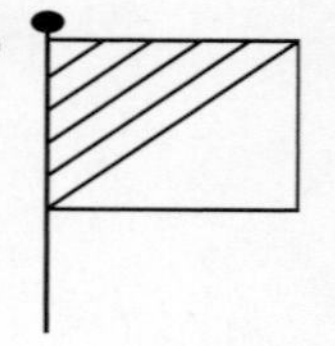

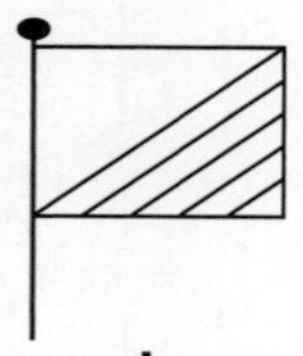

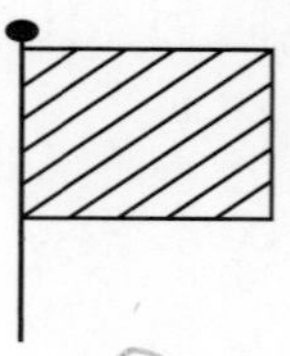

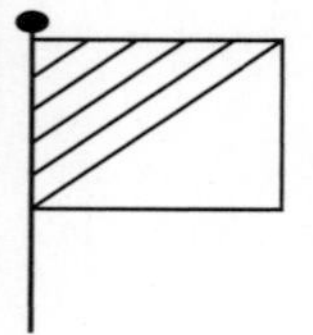

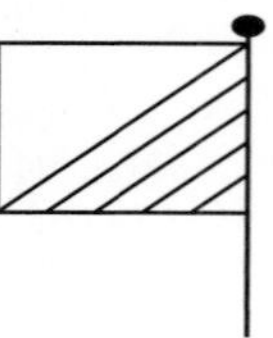

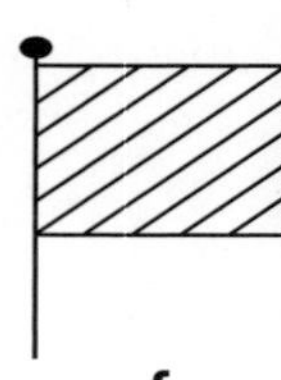

a b c d e f

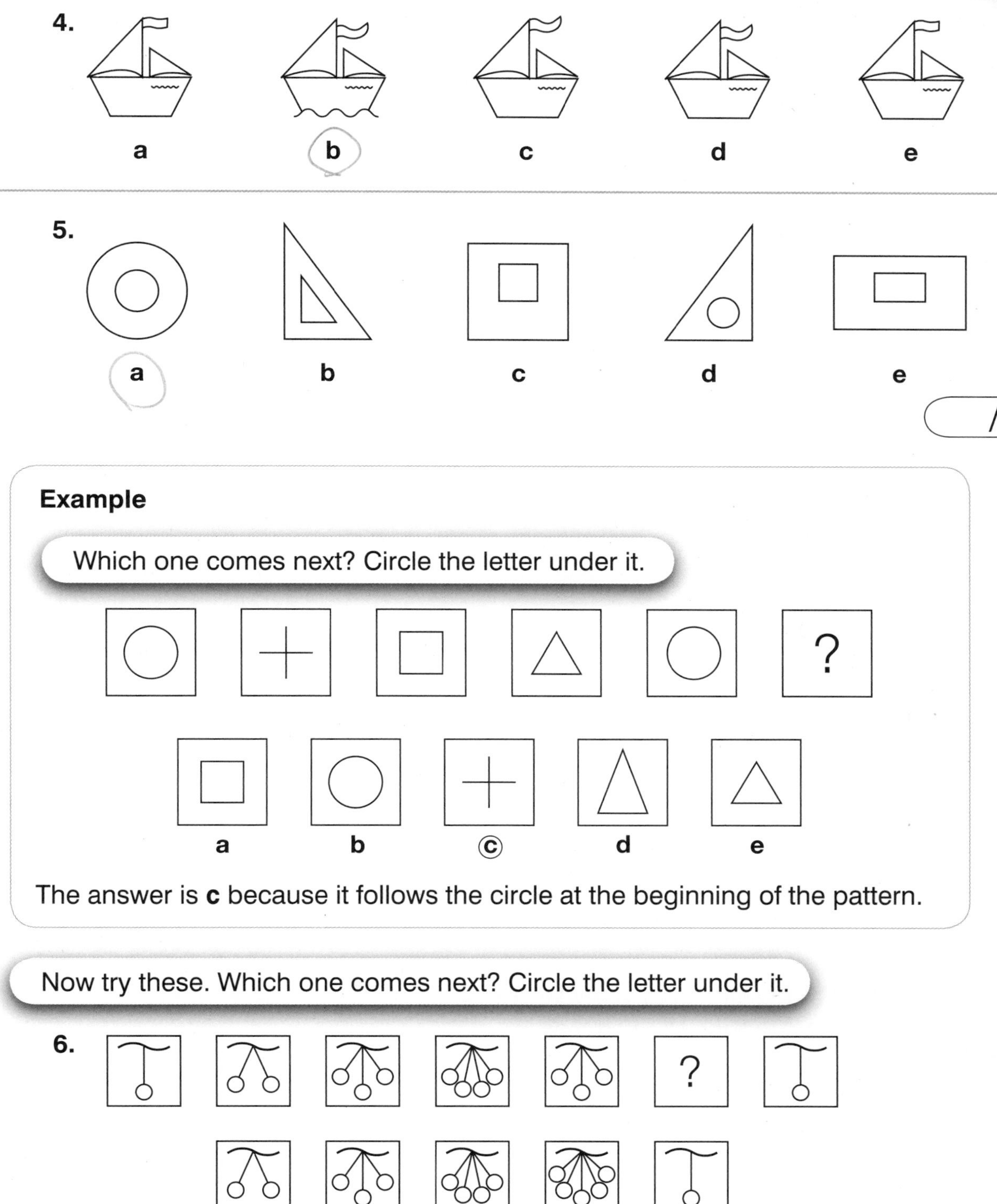
4.
a
b
c
d
e
5.
a
b
c
d
e
/5
Example
Which one comes next? Circle the letter under it.
?
a
b
c
d
e
The answer is **c** because it follows the circle at the beginning of the pattern.
Now try these. Which one comes next? Circle the letter under it.
6.
?
a
b
c
d
e

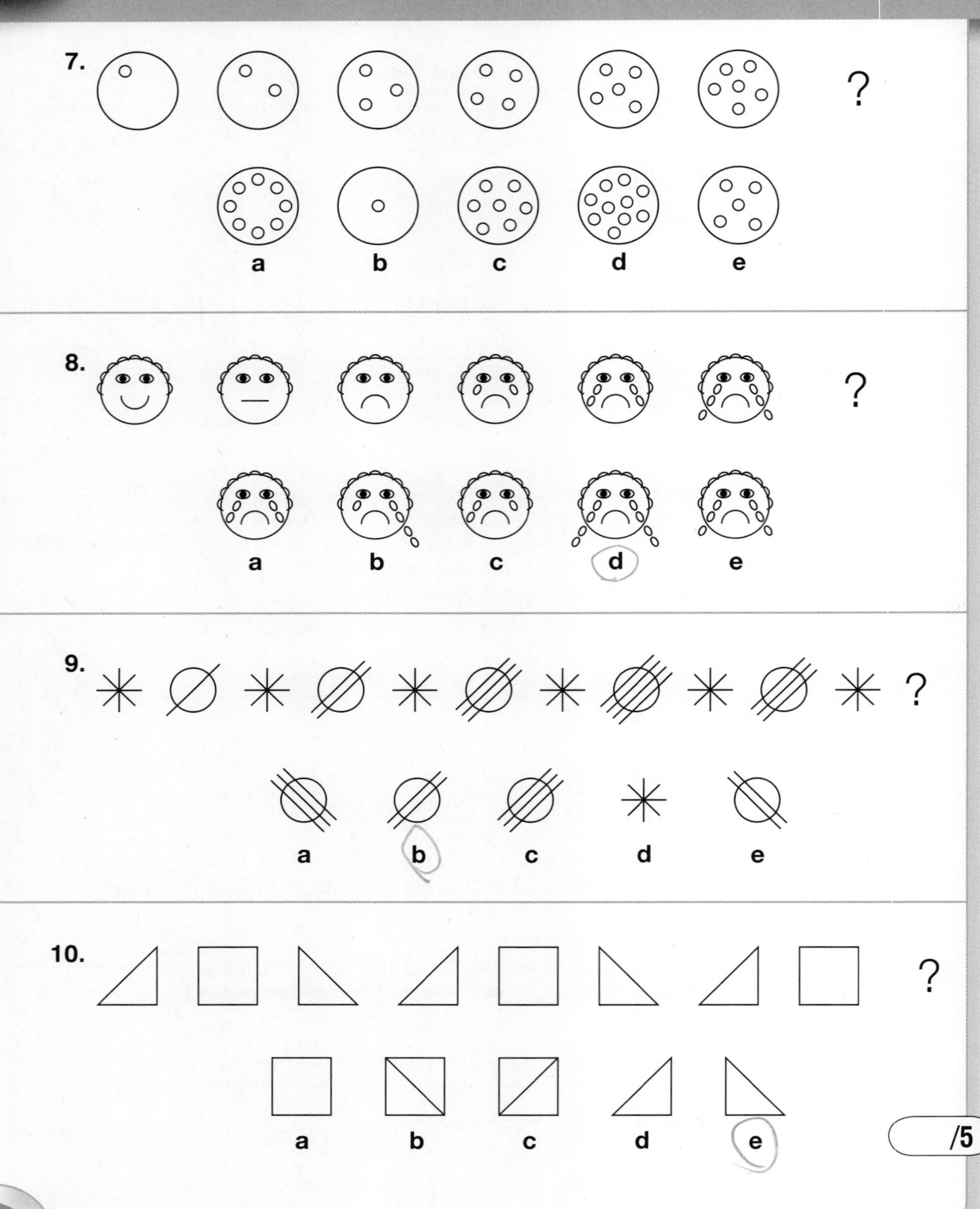
7.
?
a
b
c
d
e
8.
?
a
b
c
d
e
9.
?
a
b
c
d
e
10.
?
a
b
c
d
e
/5

Example

Complete the grid by finding the missing square. Circle the letter under the square.

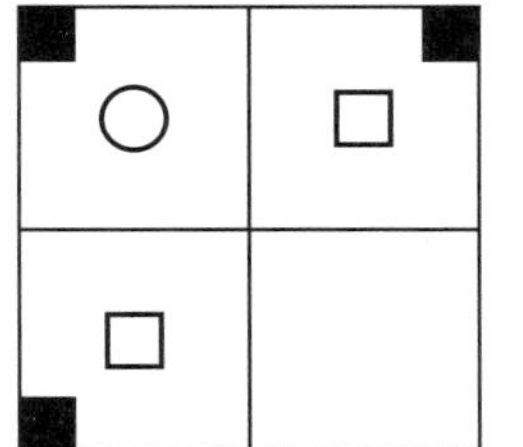

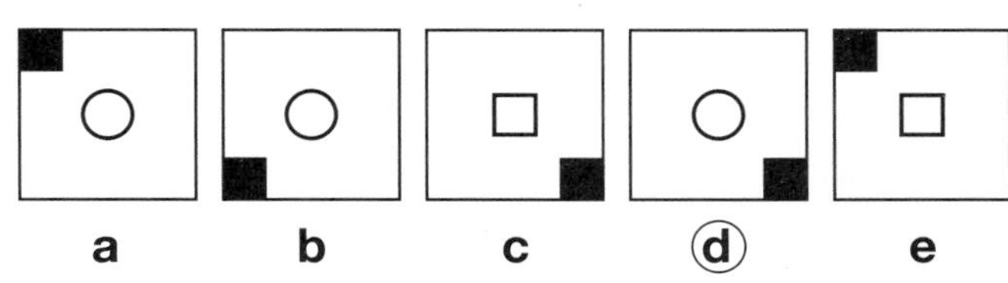

a b c (d) e

The answer is **d** because the small black squares make a pattern on the outer corners of the whole grid.

The middle of the missing part is a circle. The top of the grid is a circle and a square, so the bottom line becomes a square and then a circle.

Now try these. Circle the letter under the missing square.

11. 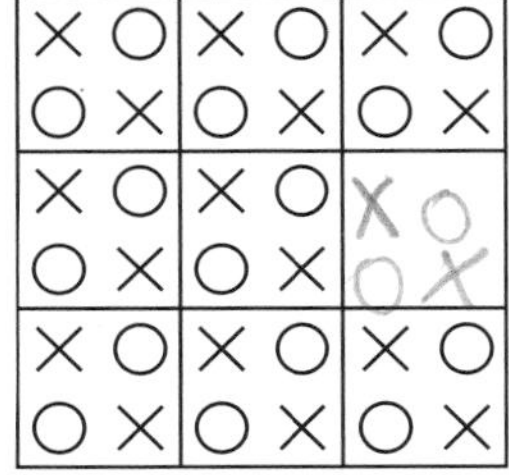

a b c d e

12. 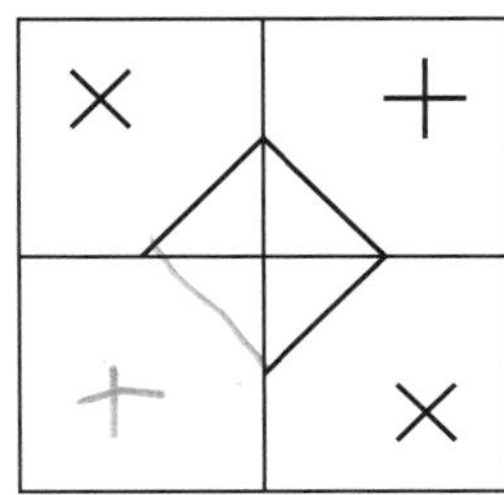

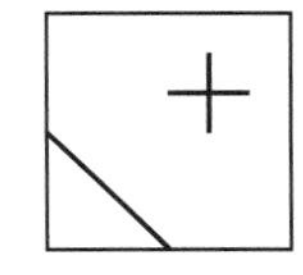 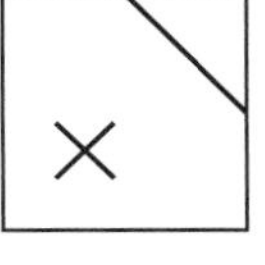 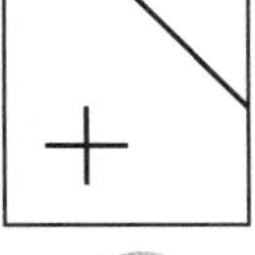 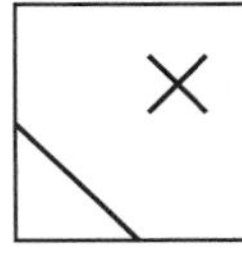 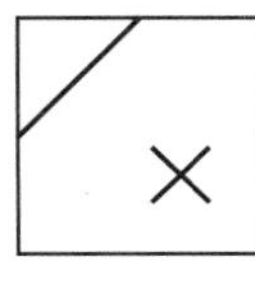

a b c d e

13.

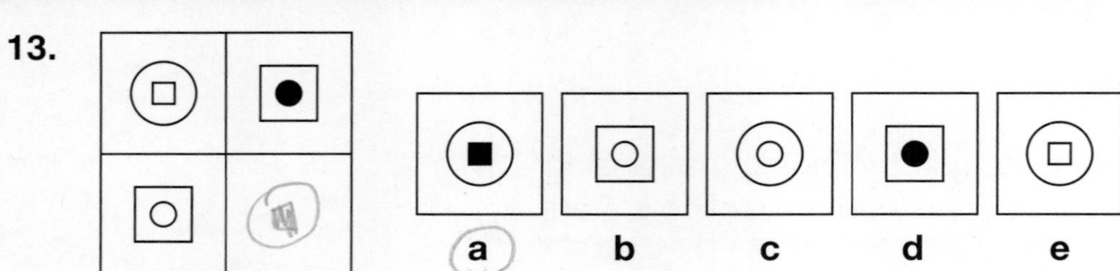

14.

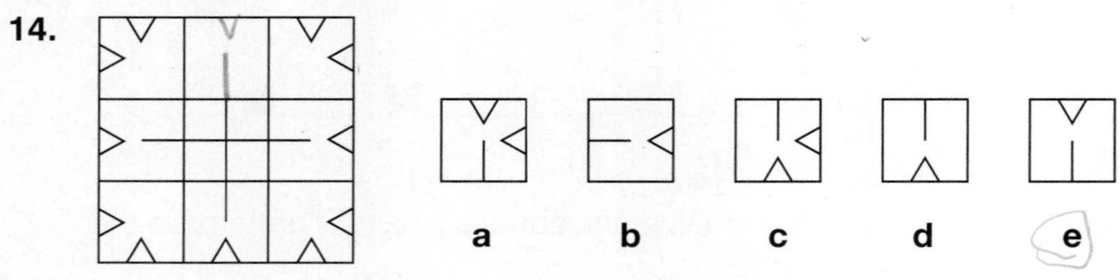

15.

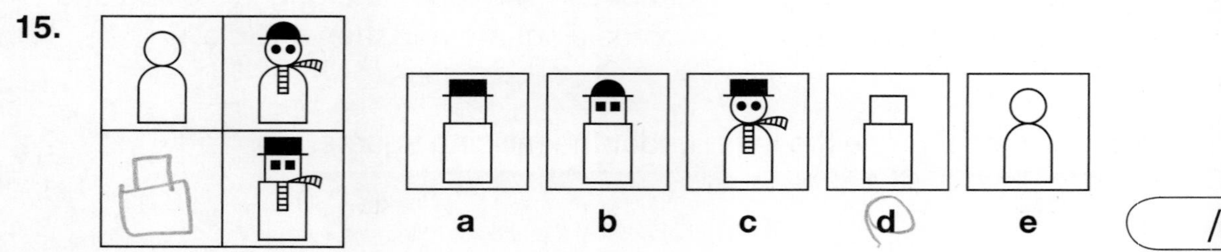

/5

Example

Match the missing part of the second pair in a similar way to the first pair. Circle the letter under the missing part.

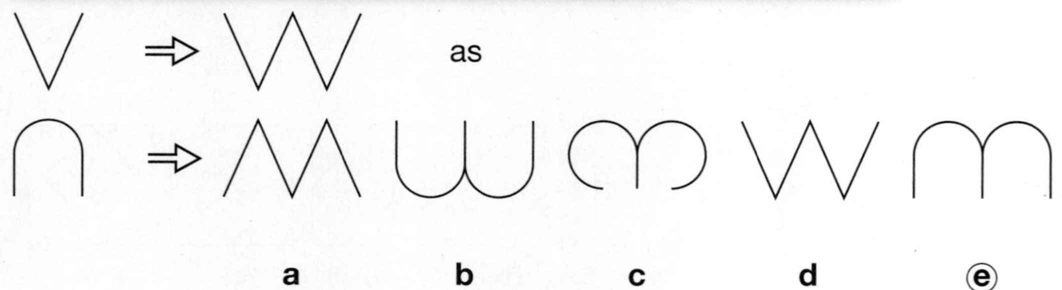

The answer is **e** because in this example, the answer is double the first one.

Now try these. Circle the letter under the missing part.

16.

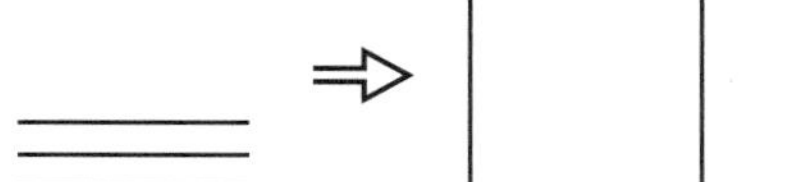

as

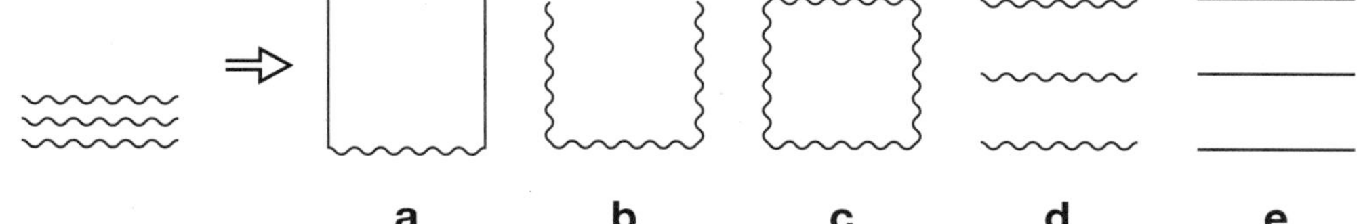

a **b** **c** **d** **e**

17.

as

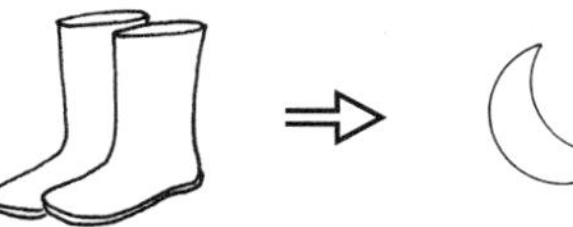

a **b** **c** **d** **e**

18.

as

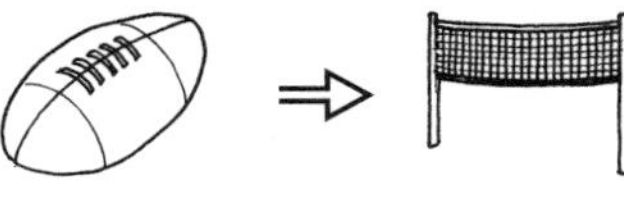

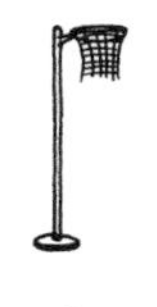

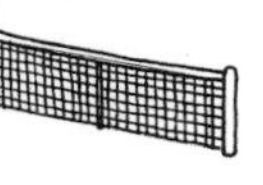

a **b** **c** **d** **e**

19.

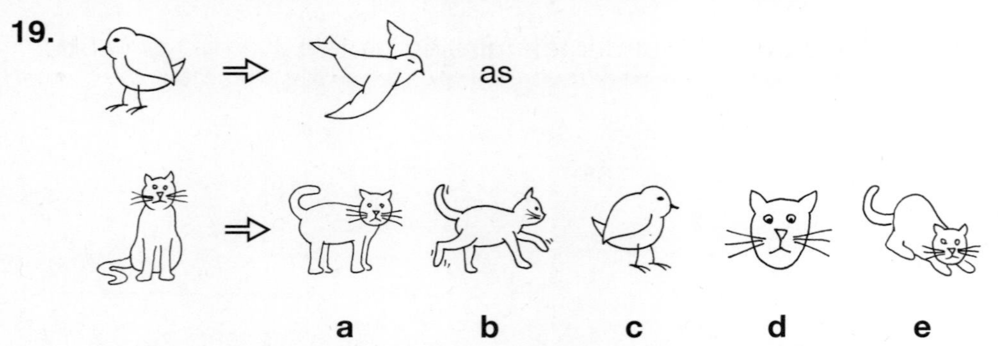

20.

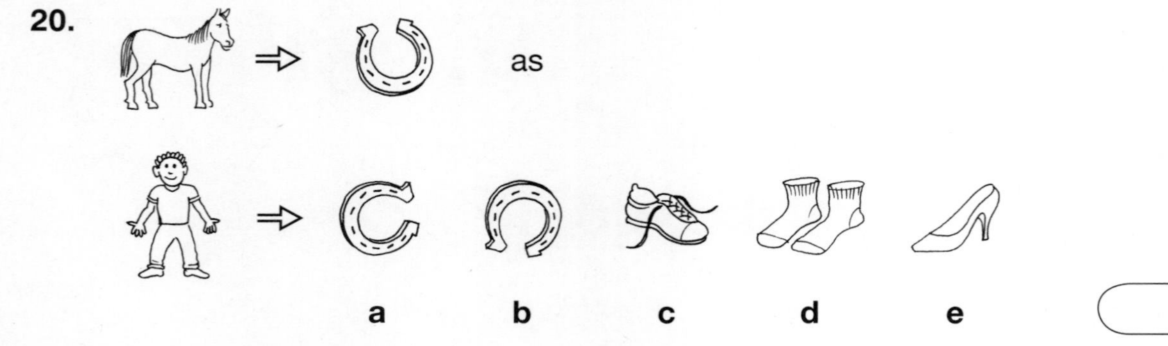

/5

Example

Look at the shapes and patterns. Work out the code by putting the pattern and shape together. Circle the letter under the code.

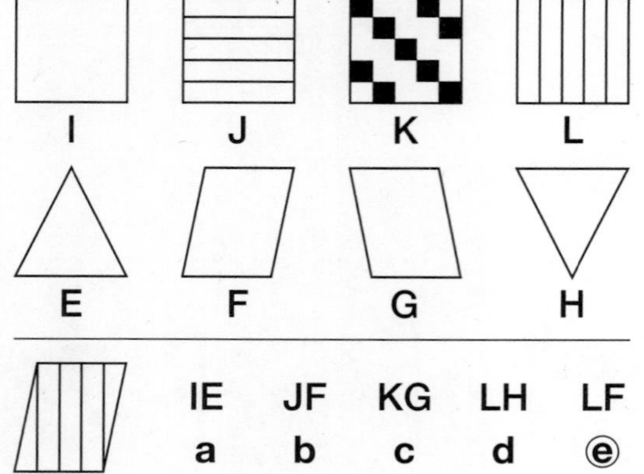

The answer is **e** because the pattern is **L** and the shape is **F**, so the code is **LF**.

Now try these. Use the shapes and patterns below to answer the questions.

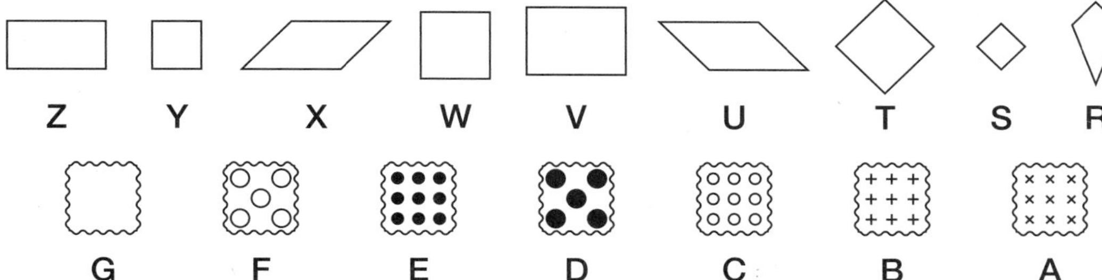

21. UF a | UC b | XC c | XG d | XF e

22. YA a | WB b | YG c | WA d | TB e

23. SF a | RC b | RF c | TC d | TD e

24. UE a | UC b | XC c | XE d | UD e

25. YA a | WB b | YG c | WA d | TB e

/5

/25

PAPER 4

Example

Which one comes next? Circle the letter under it.

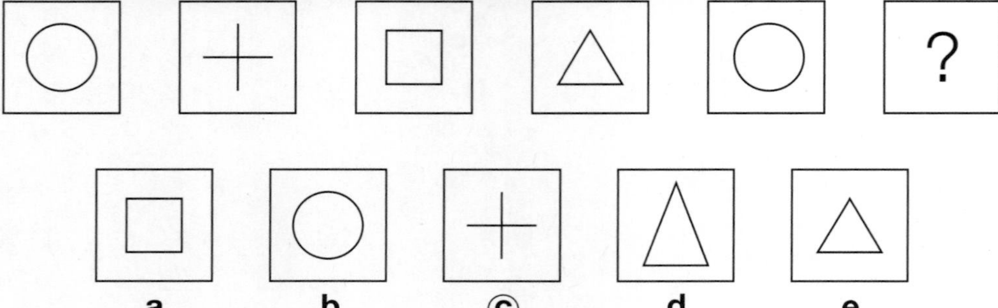

The answer is **c** because it follows the circle at the beginning of the pattern.

Now try these. Which one comes next? Circle the letter under it.

1.     

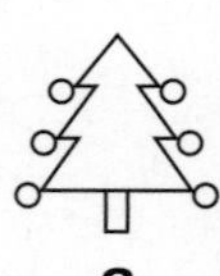   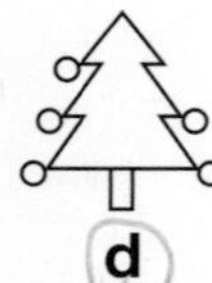 

a b c d e

2.      ?

a b c d e

3.

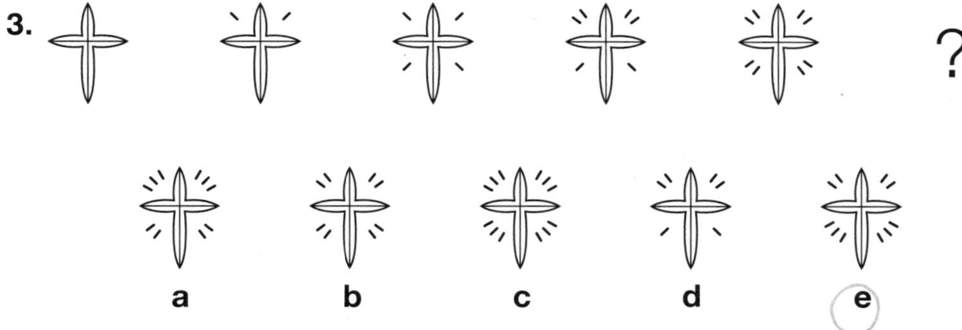

4.

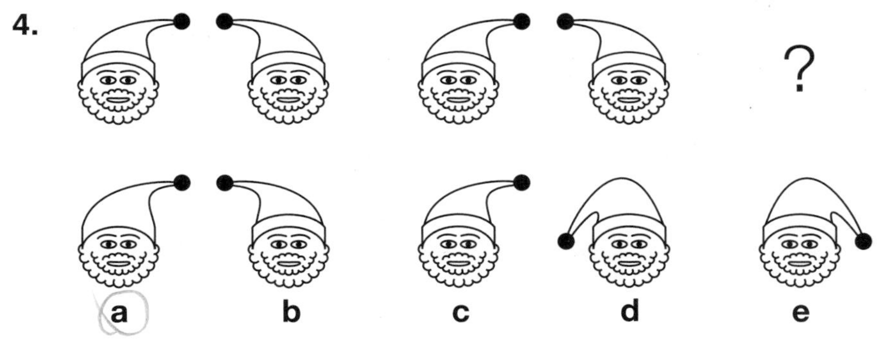

5.

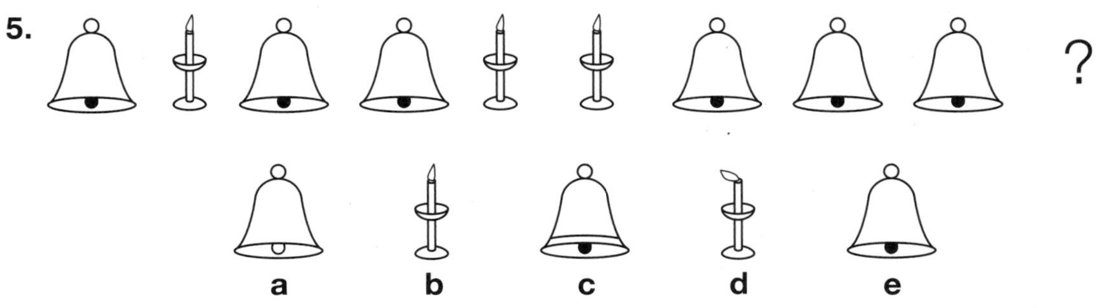

/5

Example

Complete the grid by finding the missing square. Circle the letter under the square.

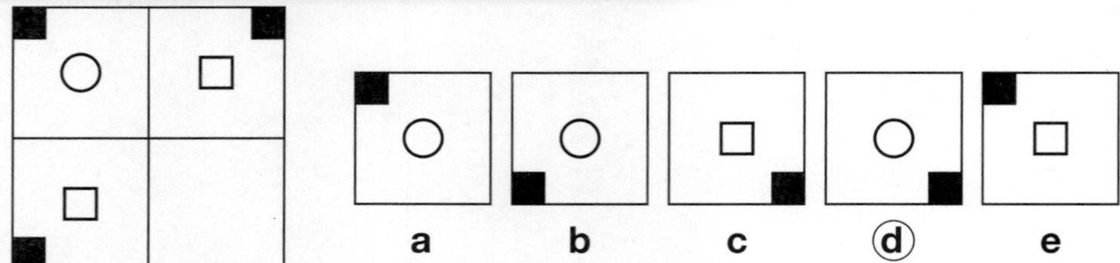

The answer is **d** because the small black squares make a pattern on the outer corners of the whole grid.

The middle of the missing part is a circle. The top of the grid is a circle and a square, so the bottom line becomes a square and then a circle.

Now try these. Circle the letter under the missing square.

6.

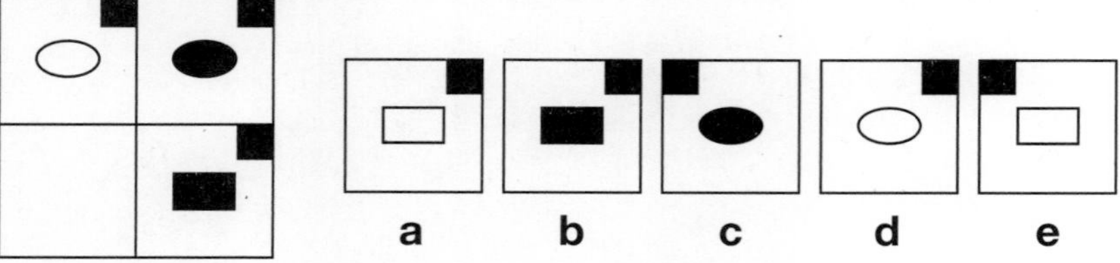

7.

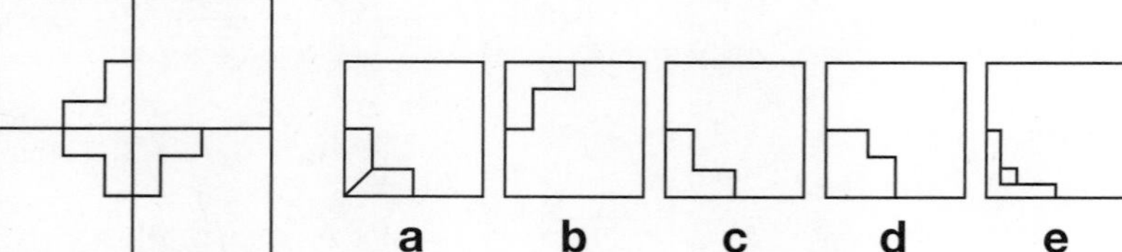

8.

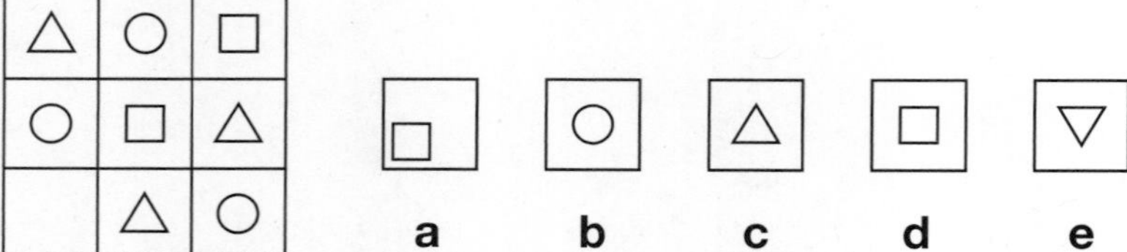

9. 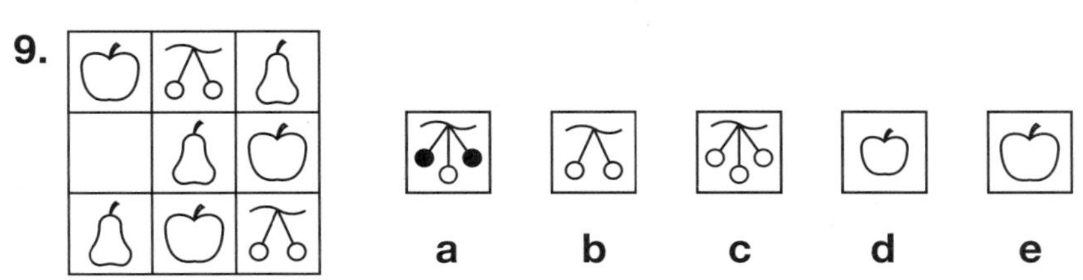

10. 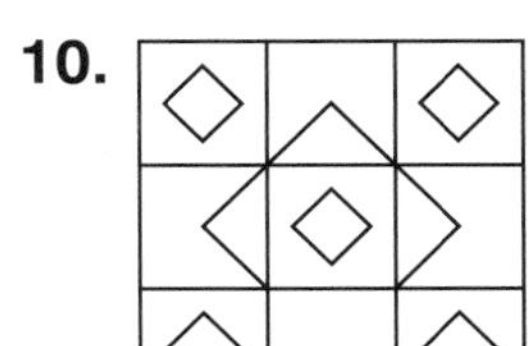

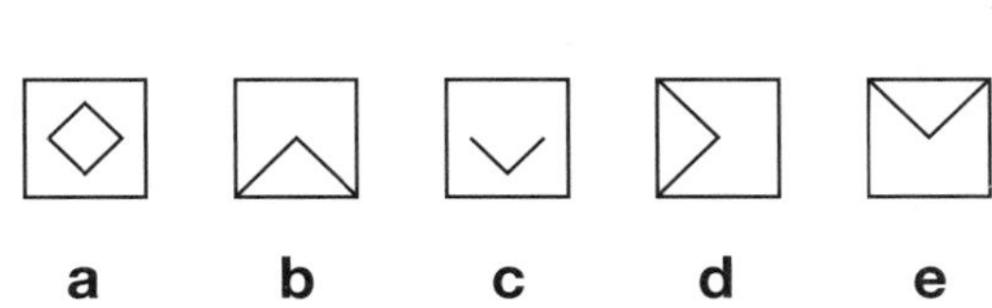

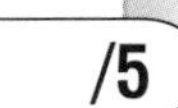

Example

Which is the odd one out? Circle the letter under it.

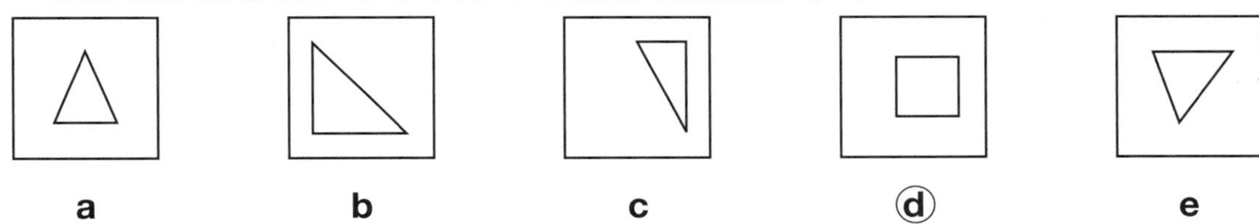

The answer is **d** because the shape inside the square has 4 sides. **a**, **b**, **c** and **e** are all similar because the shape inside each square has 3 sides.

Now try these. Which is the odd one out? Circle the letter under it.

11. 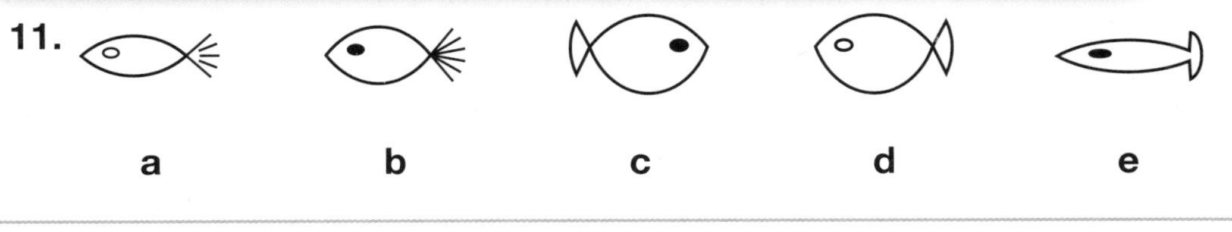

12. 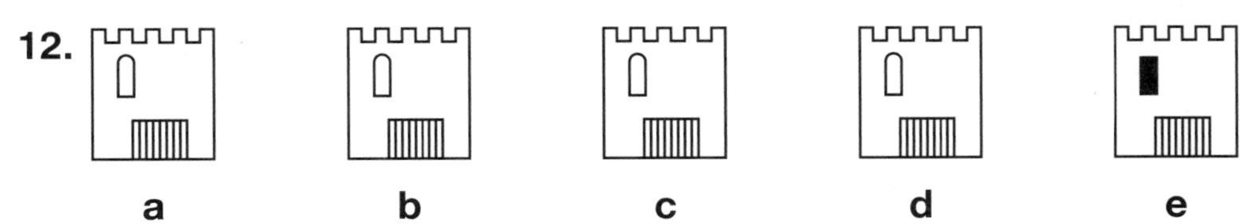

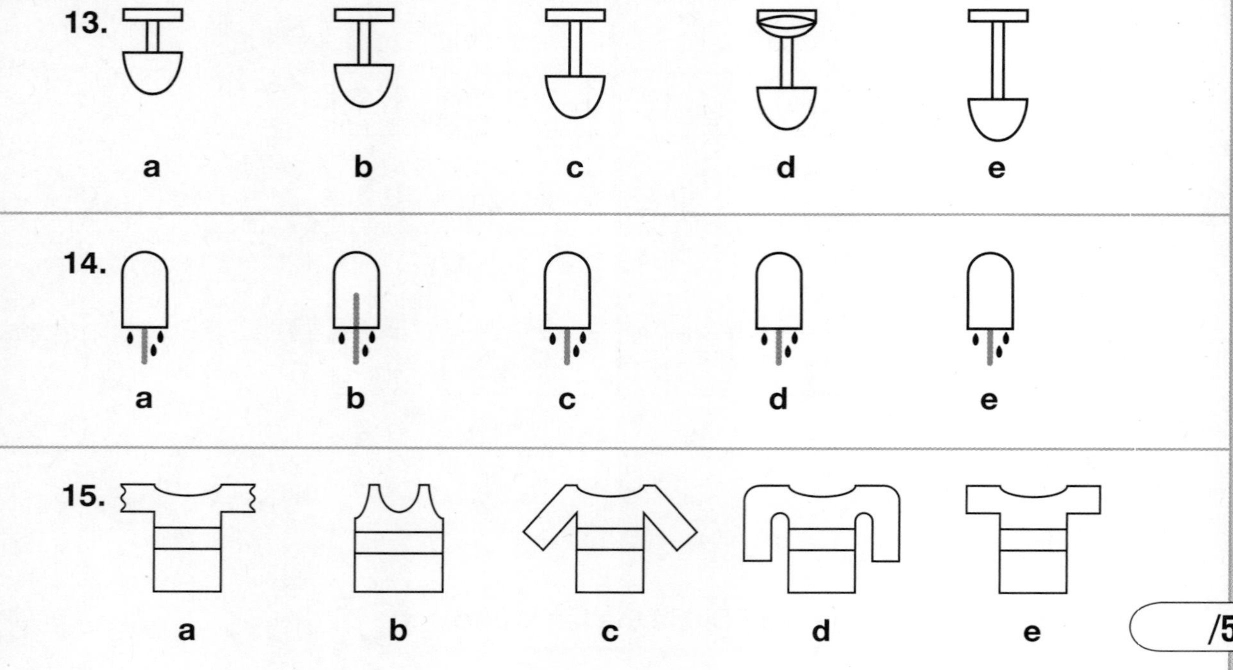

Example

Look at the shapes and patterns. Work out the code by putting the pattern and shape together. Circle the letter under the code.

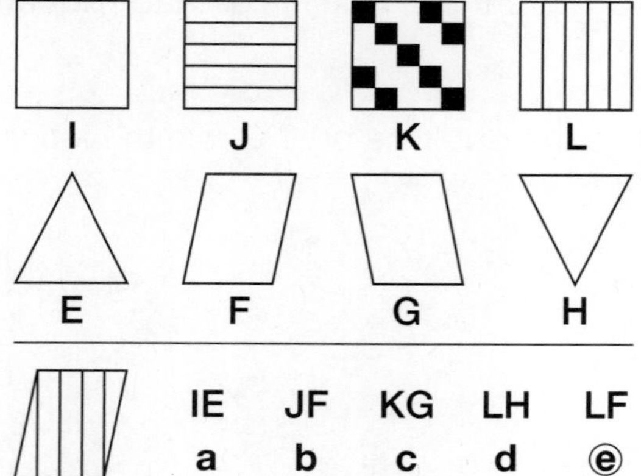

The answer is **e** because the pattern is **L** and the shape is **F**, so the code is **LF**.

Now try these. Use the shapes and patterns below to answer the questions.

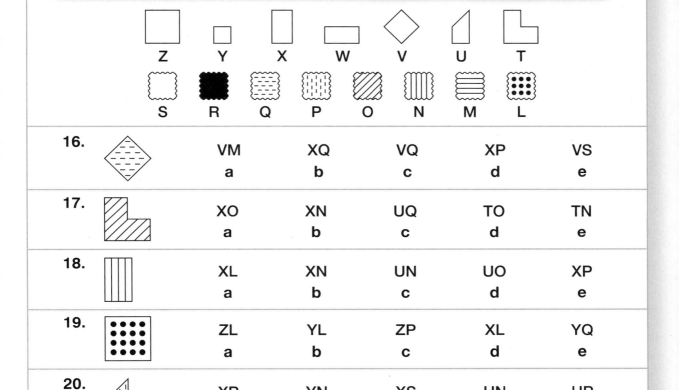

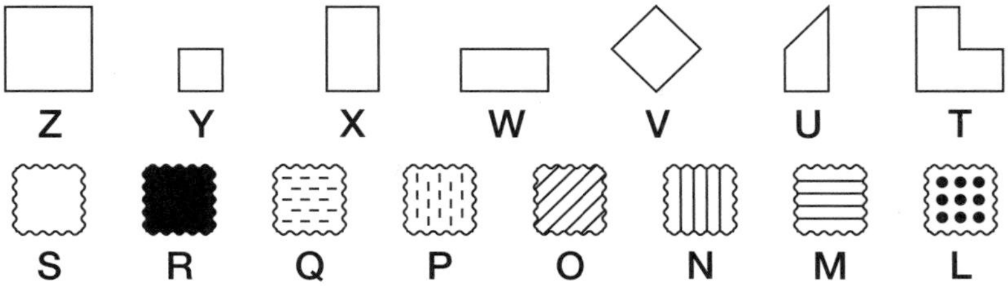

Z Y X W V U T

S R Q P O N M L

		a	b	c	d	e
16.	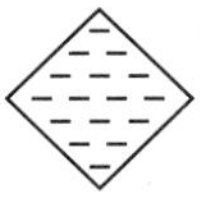	VM	XQ	VQ	XP	VS
17.	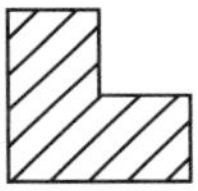	XO	XN	UQ	TO	TN
18.		XL	XN	UN	UO	XP
19.	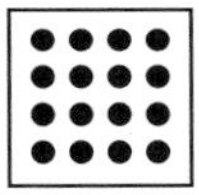	ZL	YL	ZP	XL	YQ
20.		XP	YN	XS	UN	UP

/5

Example

Match the missing part of the second pair in a similar way to the first pair. Circle the letter under the missing part.

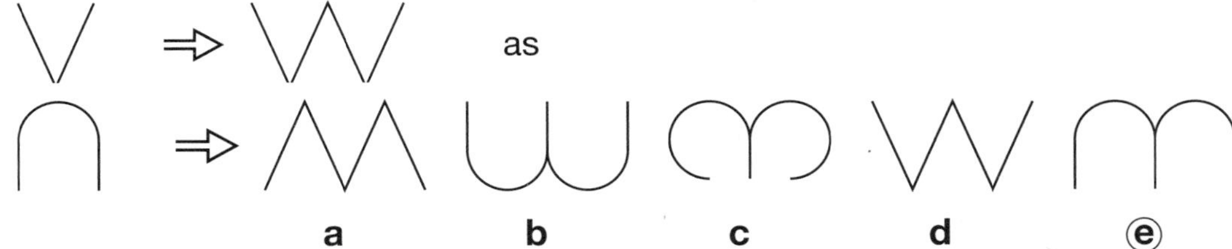

The answer is **e** because in this example, the answer is double the first one.

Now try these. Circle the letter under the missing part.

21. 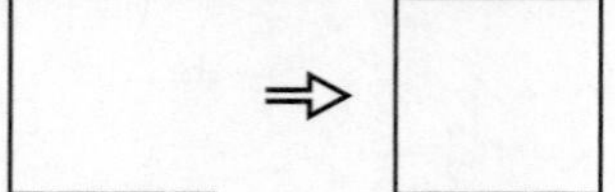 as

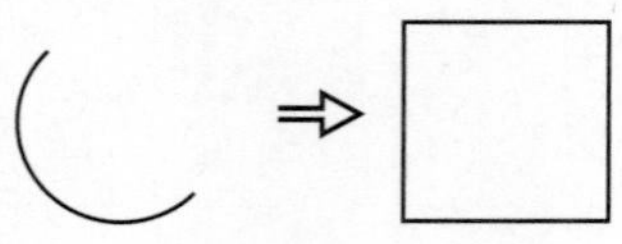  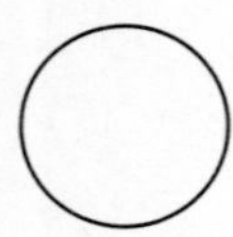  

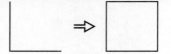

a b c d e

22.  as

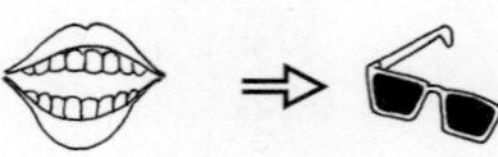    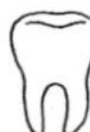

a b c d e

23. 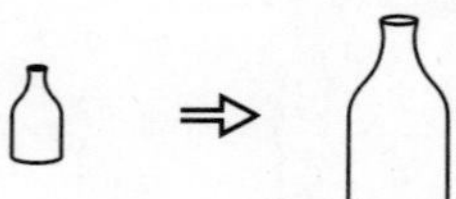 as

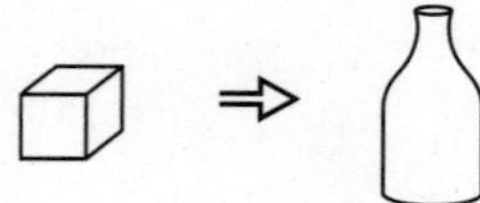 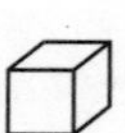 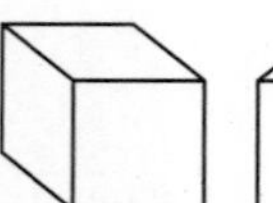

a b c d e

24.   as

a b c d e

Success

Assessment Papers

Non-Verbal Reasoning

age 7 – 8

Answer booklet

Answer booklet: Non-Verbal Reasoning age 7–8

Paper 1

1. d
2. b
3. a
4. c
5. e
6. c
7. e
8. b
9. d
10. c
11. a
12. c
13. e
14. e
15. d
16. d
17. c
18. b
19. b
20. e
21. a
22. e
23. b
24. d
25. b

Paper 2

1. d
2. b
3. a
4. d
5. e
6. d
7. d
8. b
9. e
10. a
11. a
12. c
13. e
14. b
15. d
16. b
17. c
18. e
19. d
20. b
21. c
22. a
23. b
24. e
25. d

Paper 3

1. d
2. a
3. e
4. b
5. d
6. a
7. c
8. d
9. b
10. e
11. b
12. c
13. a
14. e
15. d
16. b
17. b
18. c
19. b
20. c
21. a
22. d
23. b
24. e
25. d

Paper 4

1. d
2. b
3. a
4. c
5. b
6. a
7. c
8. d
9. b
10. e
11. c
12. e
13. d
14. b
15. b
16. c
17. d
18. b
19. a
20. e
21. c
22. b
23. e

24. c
25. a

Paper 5

1. a
2. c
3. d
4. b
5. e
6. c
7. b
8. a
9. b
10. d
11. a
12. b
13. e
14. e
15. c
16. a
17. e
18. b
19. c
20. d
21. d
22. b
23. c
24. b
25. e

Paper 6

1. c
2. d
3. a
4. e
5. c
6. a
7. c
8. d
9. e
10. b
11. c
12. e
13. a
14. b
15. a
16. d
17. c
18. e
19. c
20. a
21. e
22. c
23. c
24. a
25. d

Paper 7

1. d
2. b
3. d
4. a
5. e
6. c
7. b
8. d
9. e
10. a
11. d
12. c
13. e
14. b
15. c
16. a
17. d
18. b
19. e
20. a
21. a
22. d
23. c
24. b
25. e

Paper 8

1. c
2. e
3. a
4. d
5. b
6. c
7. d
8. d
9. a
10. b
11. b
12. c
13. e
14. c
15. d
16. c
17. d
18. a
19. b
20. e
21. a
22. c
23. e
24. b
25. d

BLANK PAGE

25.  as

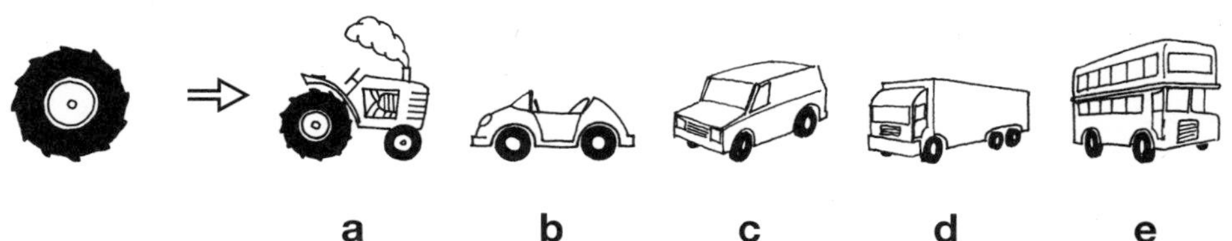

a b c d e

/5

/25

PAPER 5

Example

Look at the shapes and patterns. Work out the code by putting the pattern and shape together. Circle the letter under the code.

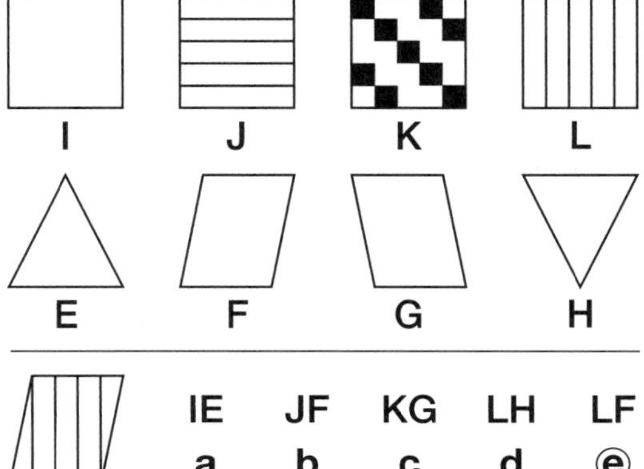

The answer is **e** because the pattern is **L** and the shape is **F**, so the code is **LF**.

Now try these. Use the shapes and patterns below to answer the questions.

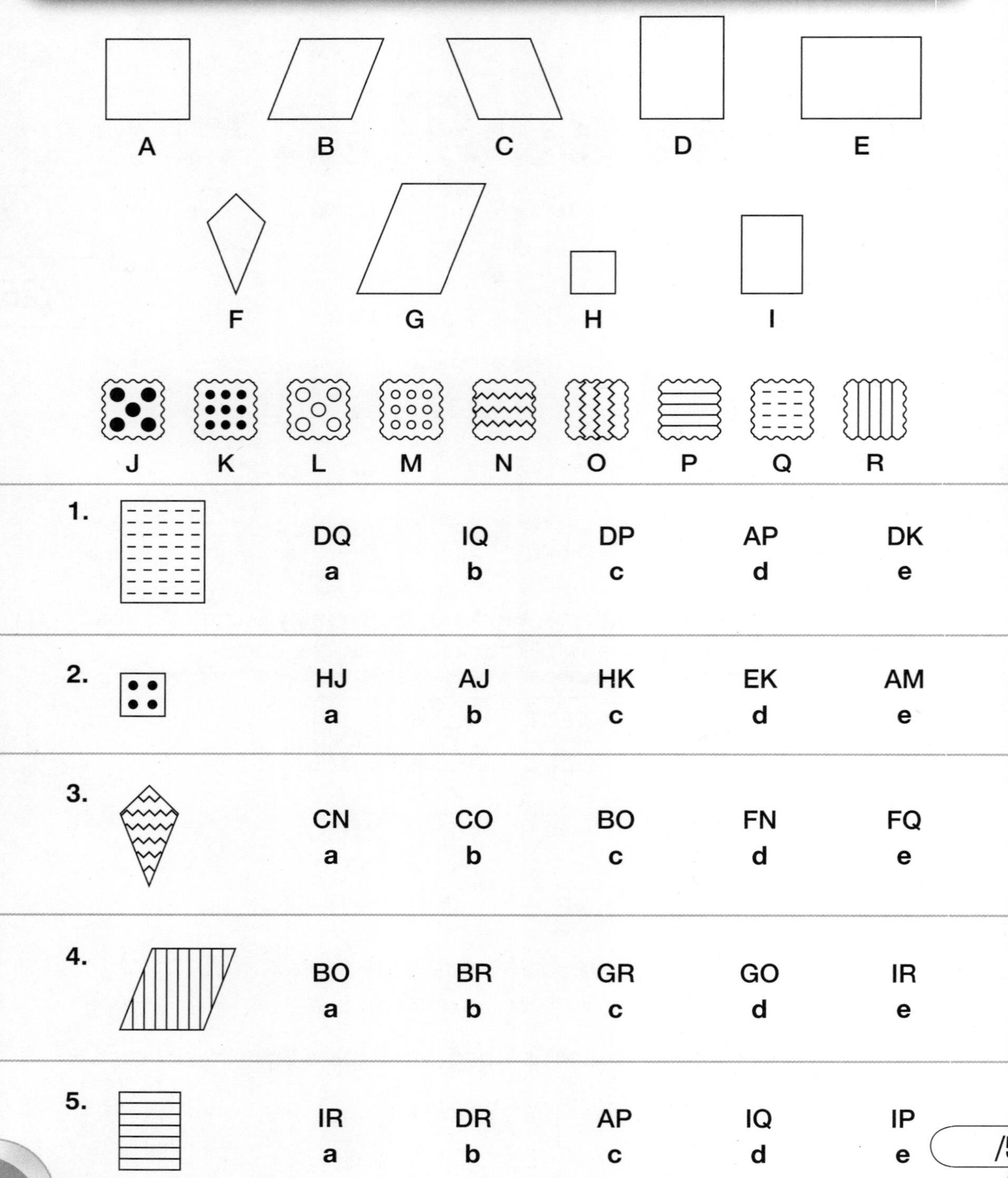

	a	b	c	d	e
1.	DQ	IQ	DP	AP	DK
2.	HJ	AJ	HK	EK	AM
3.	CN	CO	BO	FN	FQ
4.	BO	BR	GR	GO	IR
5.	IR	DR	AP	IQ	IP

/5

Example

Match the missing part of the second pair in a similar way to the first pair. Circle the letter under the missing part.

as

a **b** **c** **d** **ⓔ**

The answer is **e** because in this example, the answer is double the first one.

Now try these. Circle the letter under the missing part.

6. 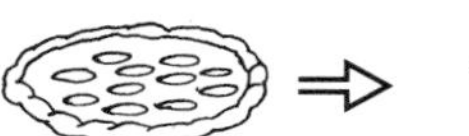  as

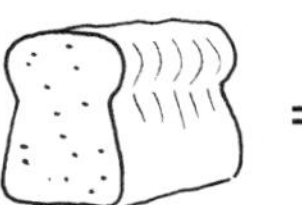    

a **b** **c** **d** **e**

7. 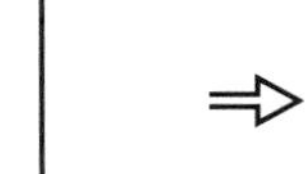 as

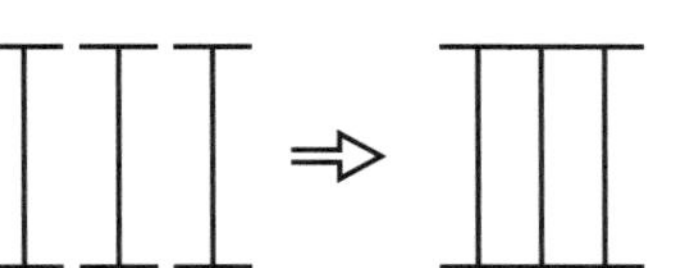   

a **b** **c** **d** **e**

8. 6 ⇒ 66 as

9 ⇒ 99 66 699 6 99

a b c d e

9.

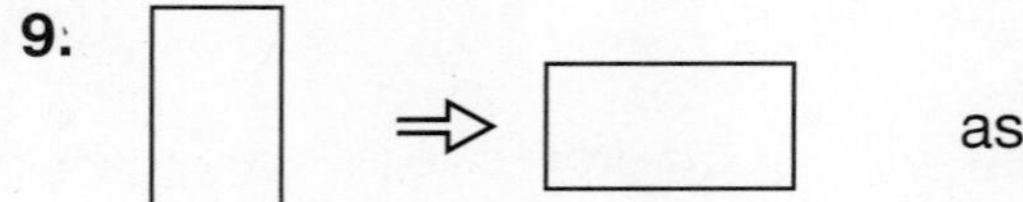

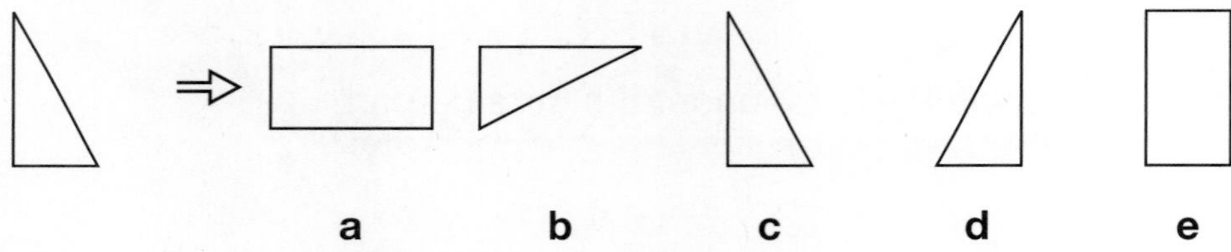

a b c d e

10. ⇒ as

⇒

a b c d e

/5

Example

Which one comes next? Circle the letter under it.

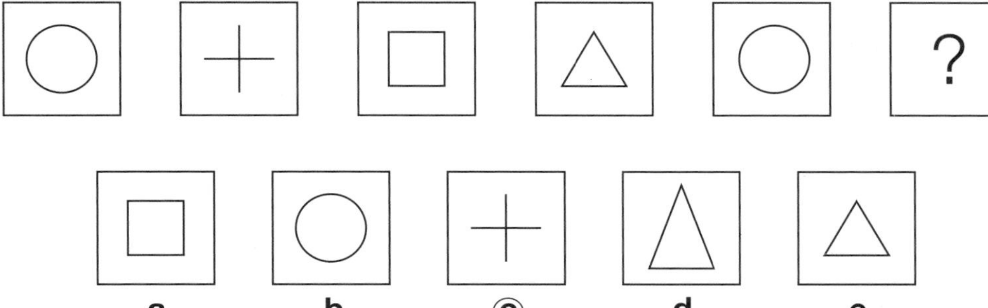

a b ⓒ d e

The answer is **c** because it follows the circle at the beginning of the pattern.

Now try these. Which one comes next? Circle the letter under it.

11. ?

a b c d e

12. ?

a b c d e

13.   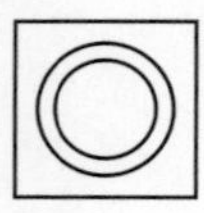 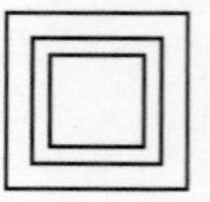 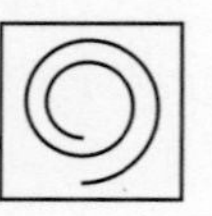  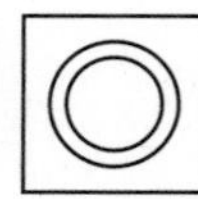 ?

 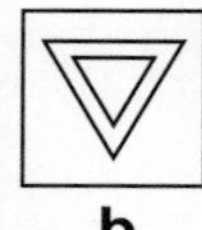  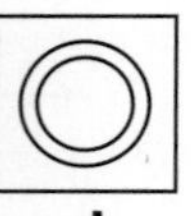 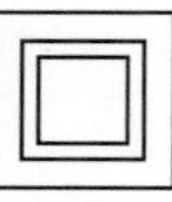

a **b** **c** **d** **e**

14. ?

a **b** **c** **d** **e**

15. 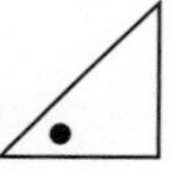 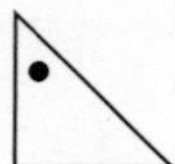 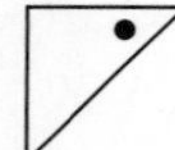 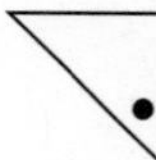 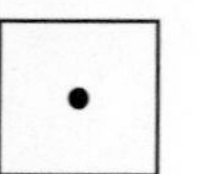 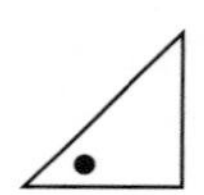 ?

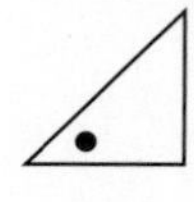 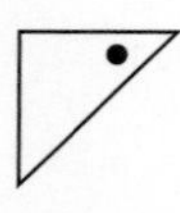 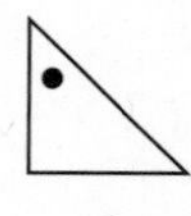 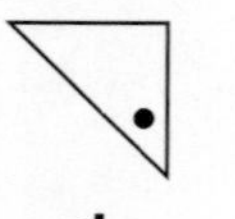

a **b** **c** **d** **e**

/5

Example

Which is the odd one out? Circle the letter under it.

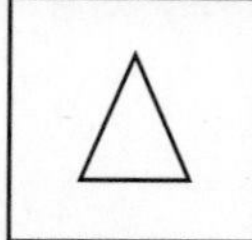 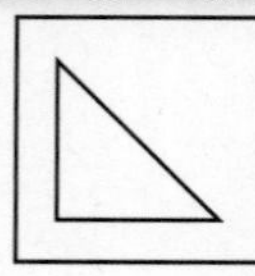 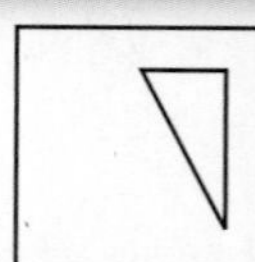 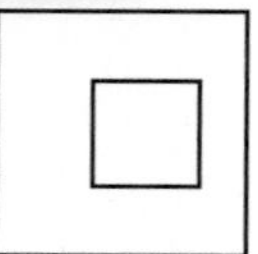 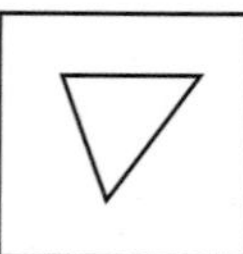

a **b** **c** **(d)** **e**

The answer is **d** because the shape inside the square has 4 sides. **a**, **b**, **c** and **e** are all similar because the shape inside each square has 3 sides.

Now try these. Which is the odd one out? Circle the letter under it.

16.  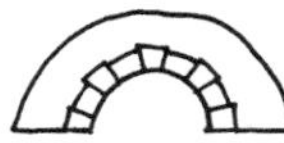  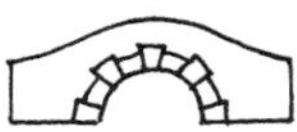 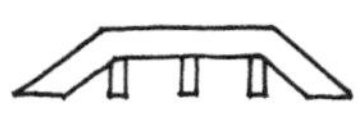

a b c d e

17.   

a b c d e

18.    

a b c d

19.     

a b c d e

20. 

a b c d e

/5

Example

Complete the grid by finding the missing square. Circle the letter under the square.

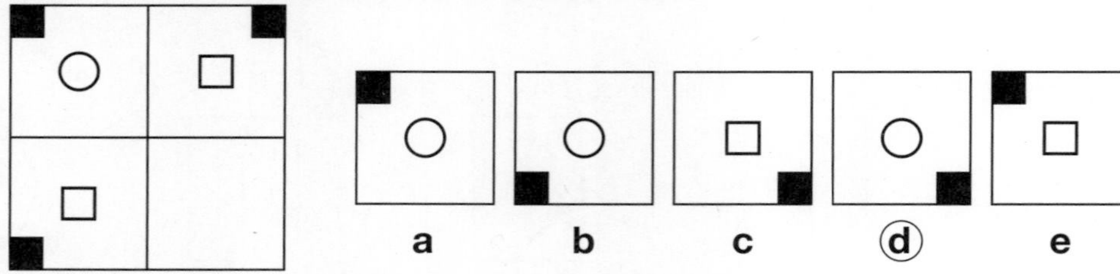

The answer is **d** because the small black squares make a pattern on the outer corners of the whole grid.

The middle of the missing part is a circle. The top of the grid is a circle and a square, so the bottom line becomes a square and then a circle.

Now try these. Circle the letter under the missing square.

21.

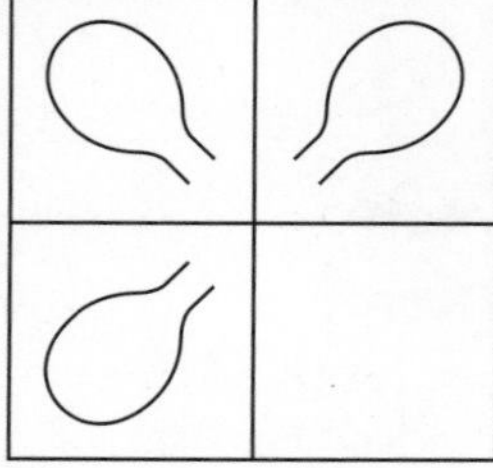

a

b

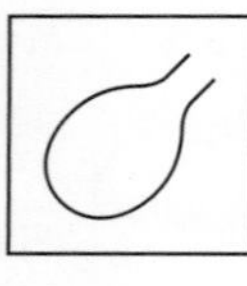
c

d

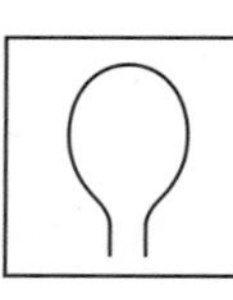
e

22.

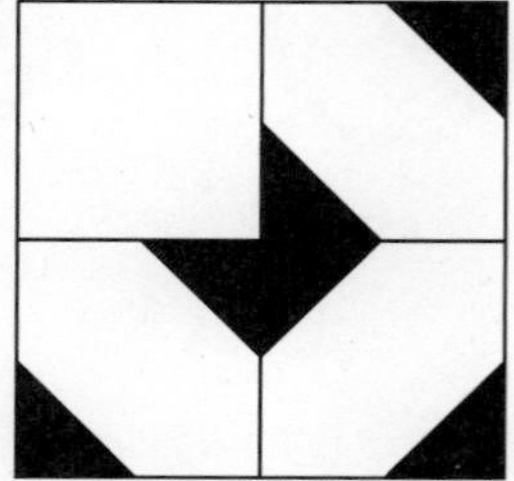

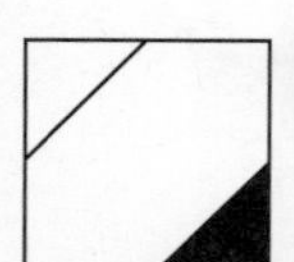
a

b

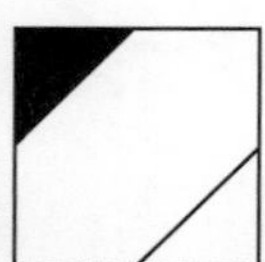
c

d

e

23. 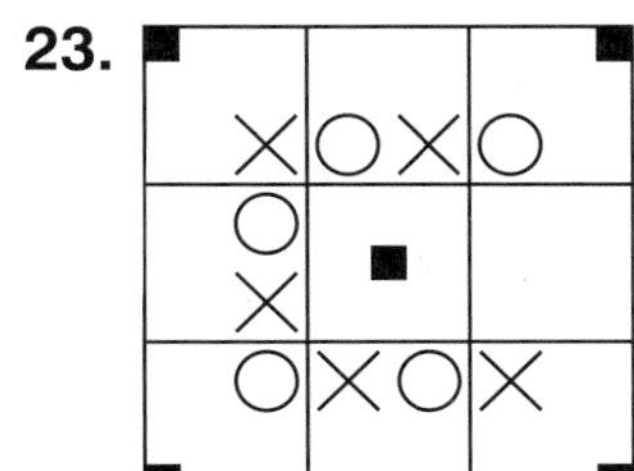

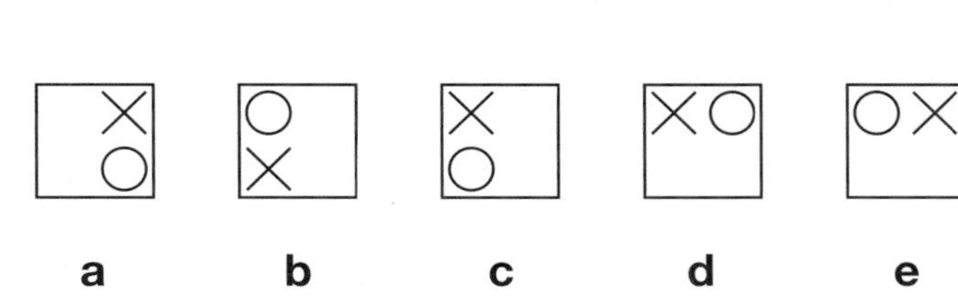

a b c d e

24. 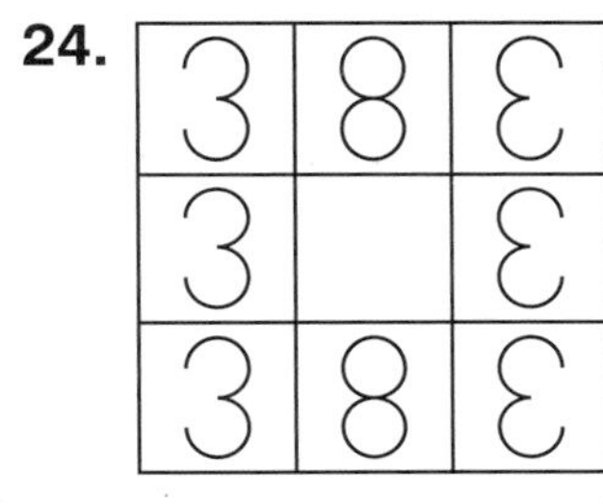

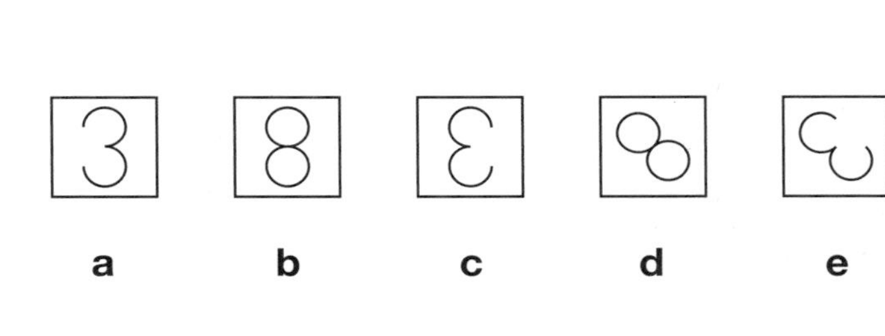

a b c d e

25. 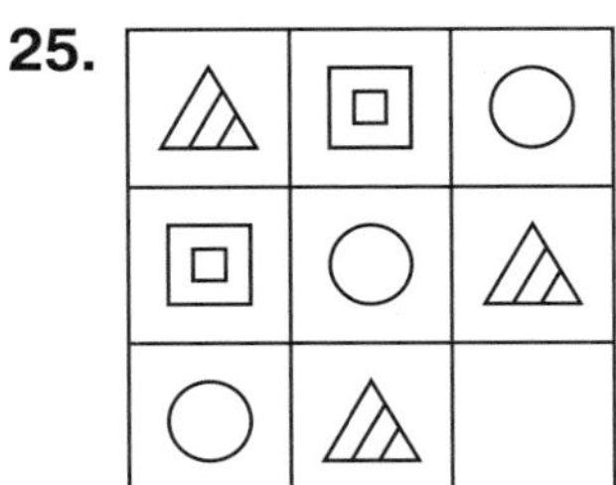

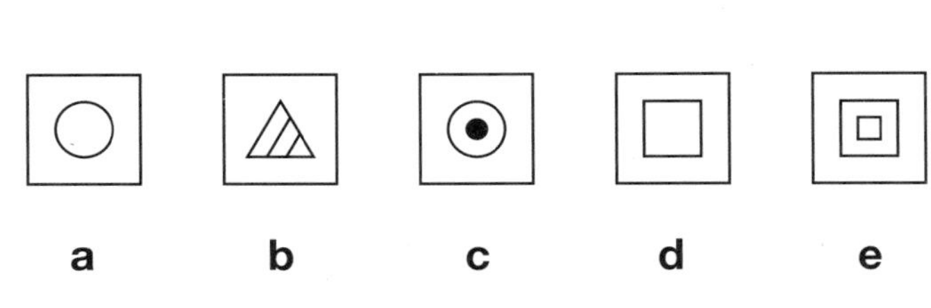

a b c d e

/5

/25

PAPER 6

Example

Match the missing part of the second pair in a similar way to the first pair. Circle the letter under the missing part.

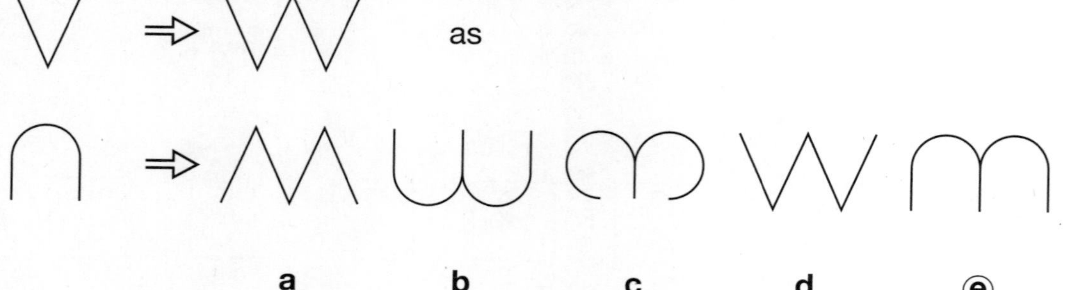

The answer is **e** because in this example, the answer is double the first one.

Now try these. Circle the letter under the missing part.

1.    as

a b c d e

2.   as

   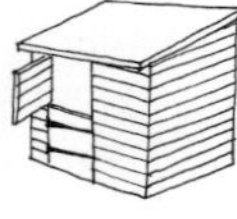 

a b c d e

3. 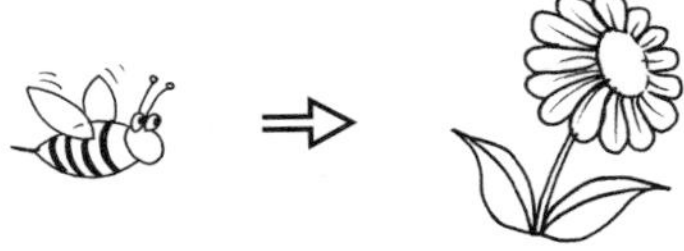 as

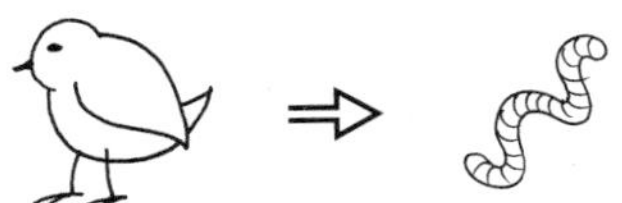   

a **b** **c** **d** **e**

4.  as

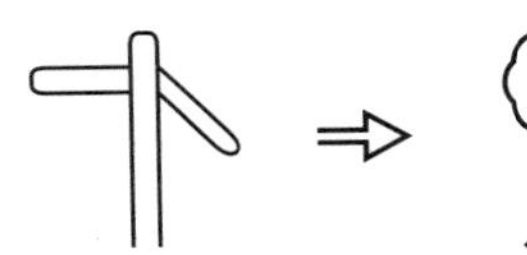  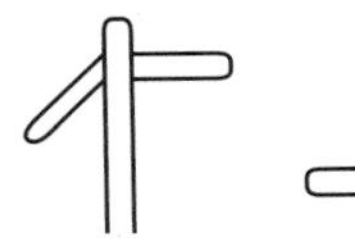 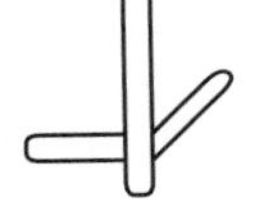

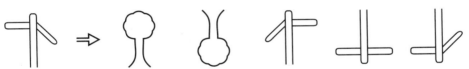

a **b** **c** **d** **e**

5. 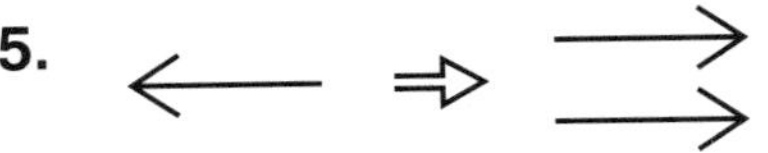 as

 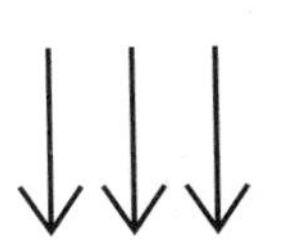

a **b** **c** **d** **e**

/5

Example

Look at the shapes and patterns. Work out the code by putting the pattern and shape together. Circle the letter under the code.

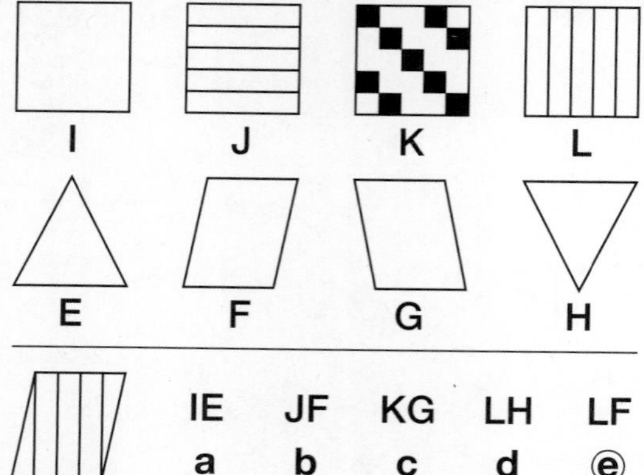

The answer is **e** because the pattern is **L** and the shape is **F**, so the code is **LF**.

Now try these. Use the shapes and patterns below to answer the questions.

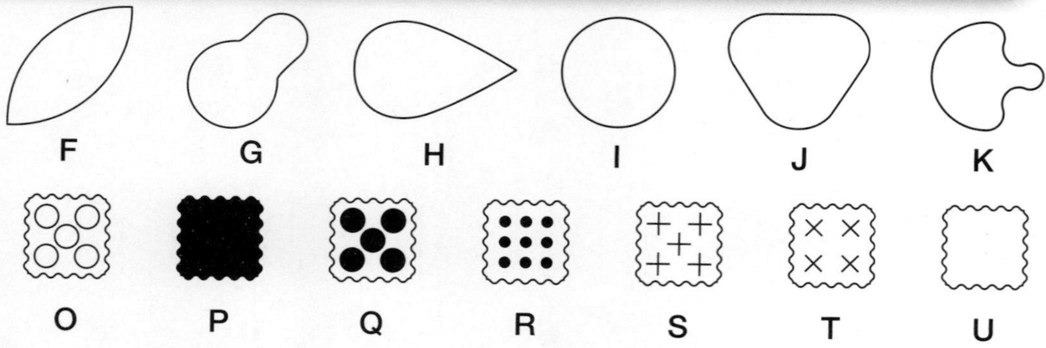

6.

FR	HR	FQ	FP	HO
a	b	c	d	e

7. 

KU	HT	KT	HR	KS
a	b	c	d	e

8. 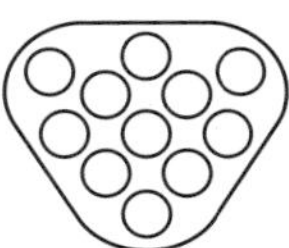

GP	GR	IS	JO	JP
a	b	c	d	e

9. 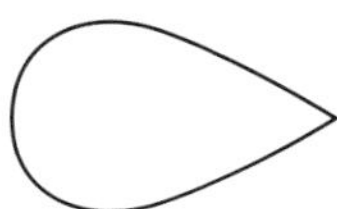

HO	FU	FO	KU	HU
a	b	c	d	e

10. 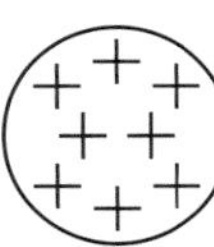

IT	IS	HU	FS	JS
a	b	c	d	e

/5

Example

Which one comes next? Circle the letter under it.

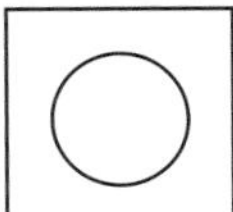 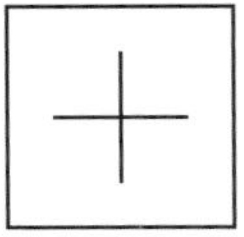 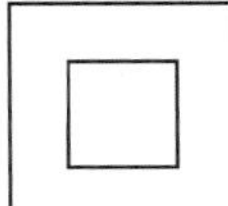 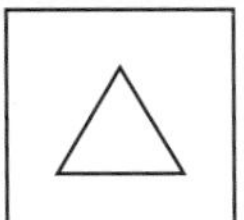 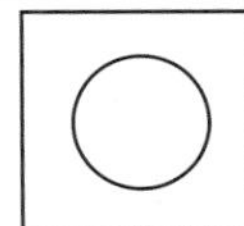 

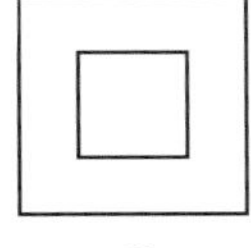  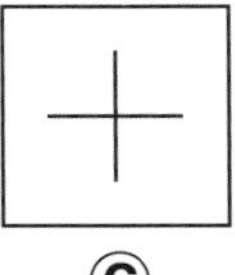 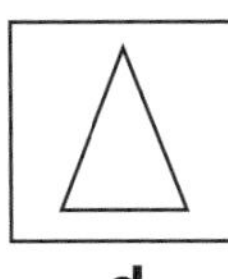 

a b ⓒ d e

The answer is **c** because it follows the circle at the beginning of the pattern.

Now try these. Which one comes next? Circle the letter under it.

11. ?

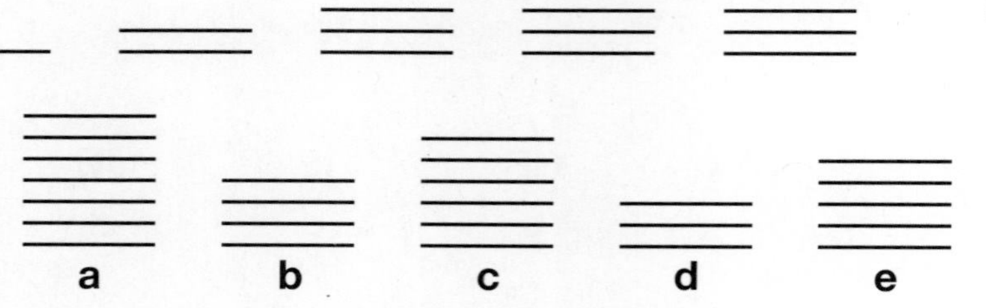

a b c d e

12.

 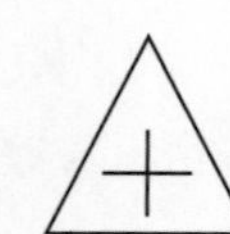     ?

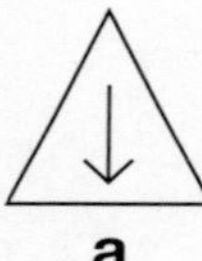 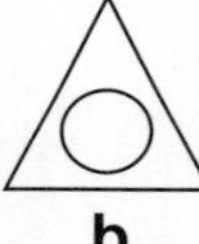  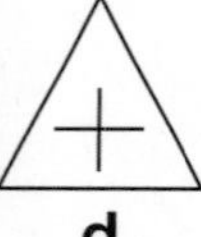

a b c d e

13.

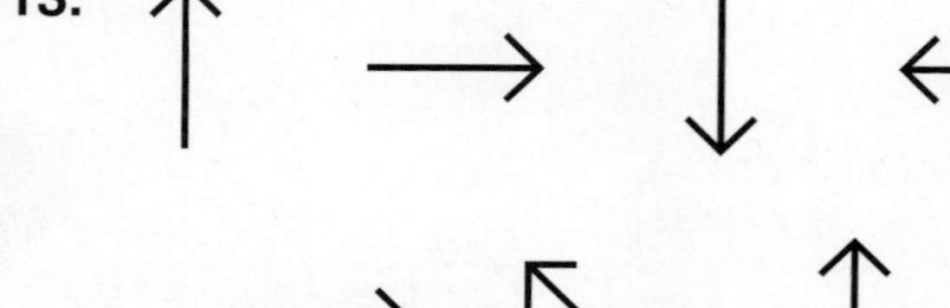  ?

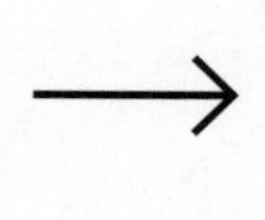  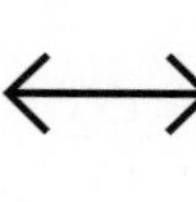

a b c d e

14. ?

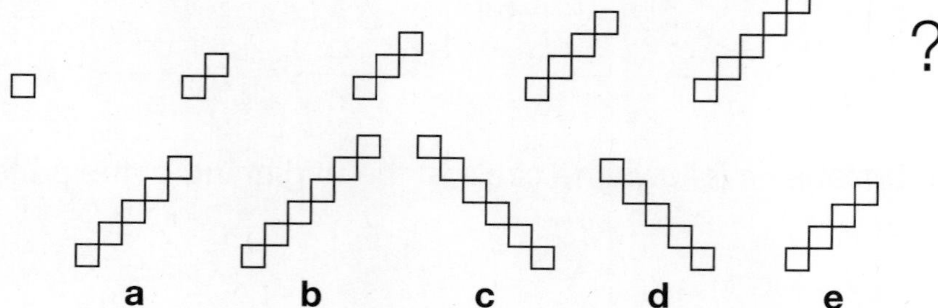

a b c d e

15. 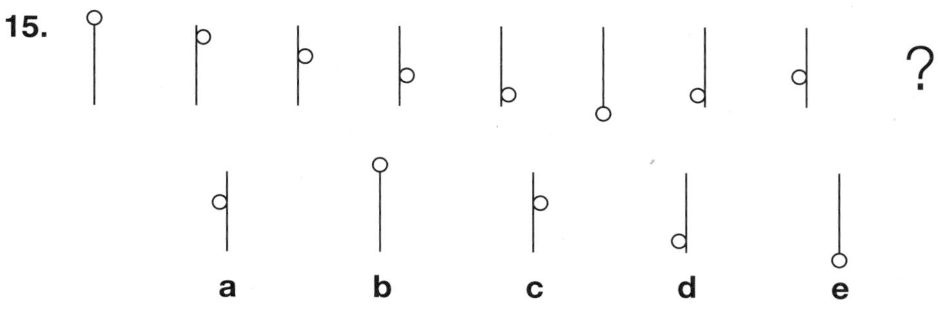

/5

Example

Complete the grid by finding the missing square.
Circle the letter under the square.

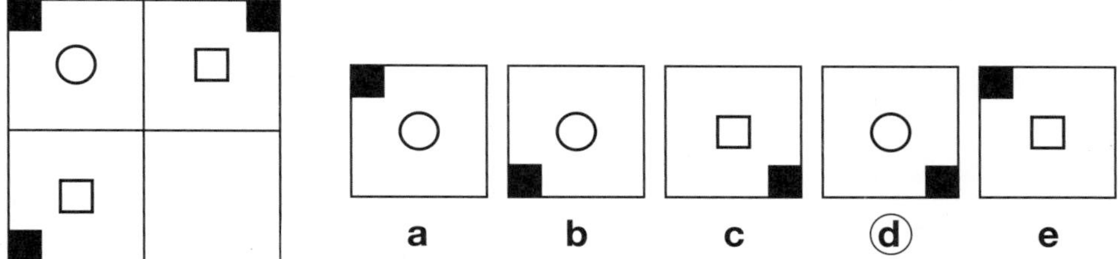

The answer is **d** because the small black squares make a pattern on the outer corners of the whole grid.

The middle of the missing part is a circle. The top of the grid is a circle and a square, so the bottom line becomes a square and then a circle.

Now try these. Circle the letter under the missing square.

16.

a

b

c

d

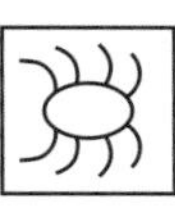
e

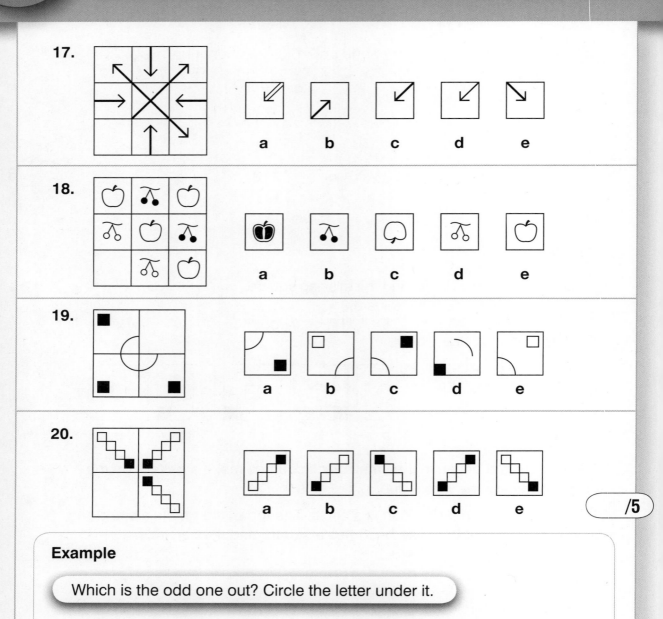

17.

a b c d e

18.

a b c d e

19.

a b c d e

20.

a b c d e

/5

Example

Which is the odd one out? Circle the letter under it.

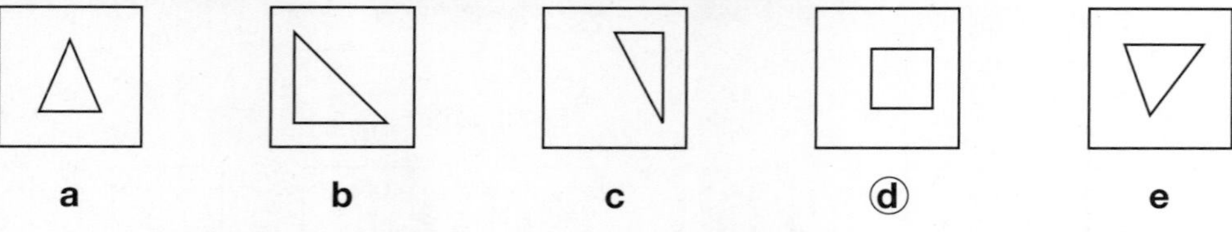

a b c (d) e

The answer is **d** because the shape inside the square has 4 sides. **a**, **b**, **c** and **e** are all similar because the shape inside each square has 3 sides.

Now try these. Which is the odd one out? Circle the letter under it.

21.

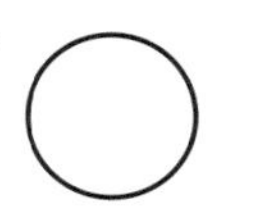			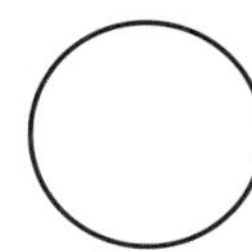	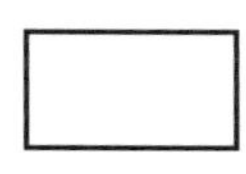
a	b	c	d	e

22.

a	b	c	d	e

23.

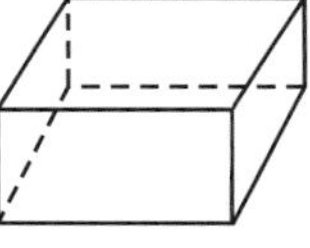	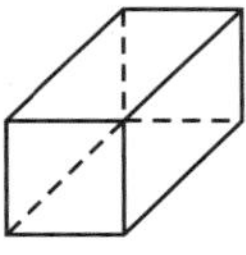	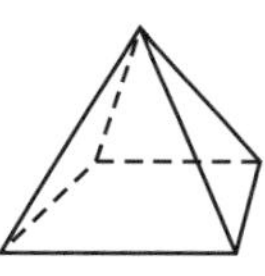	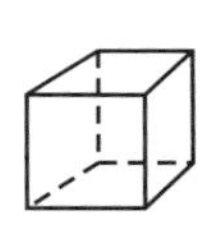	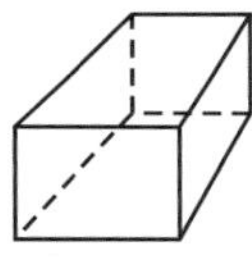
a	b	c	d	e

24.

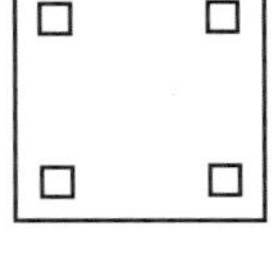	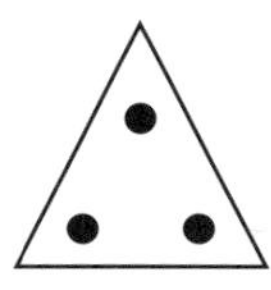	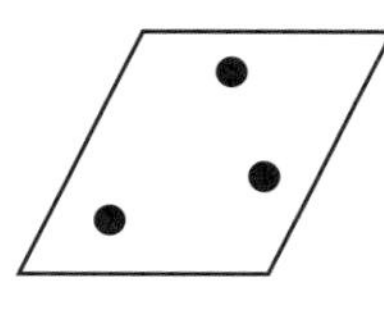	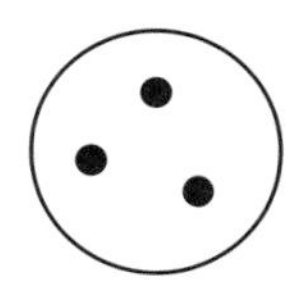	
a	b	c	d	e

25.

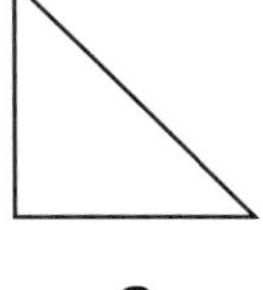	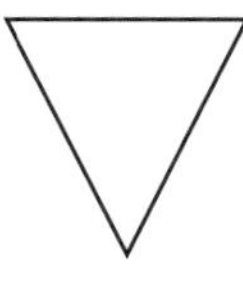	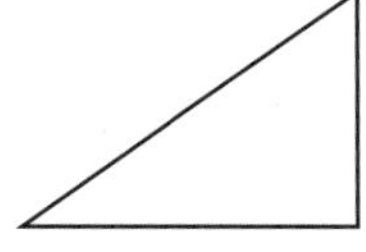	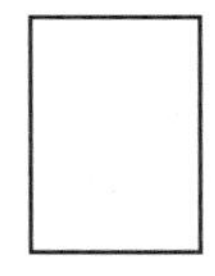	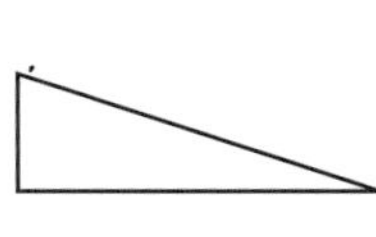
a	b	c	d	e

/5

/25

PAPER 7

Example

Which one comes next? Circle the letter under it.

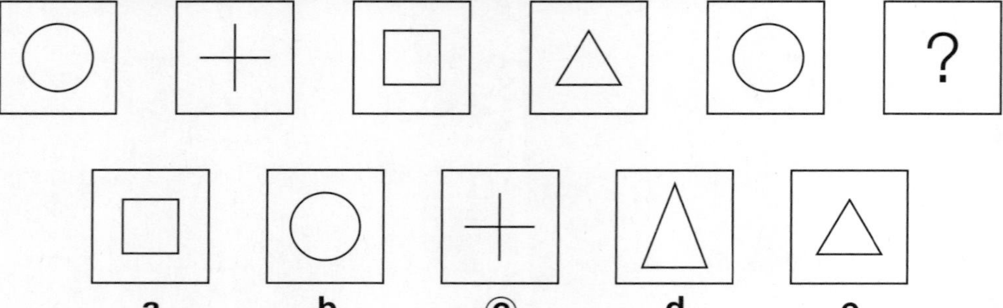

The answer is **c** because it follows the circle at the beginning of the pattern.

Now try these. Which one comes next? Circle the letter under it.

1.

2.

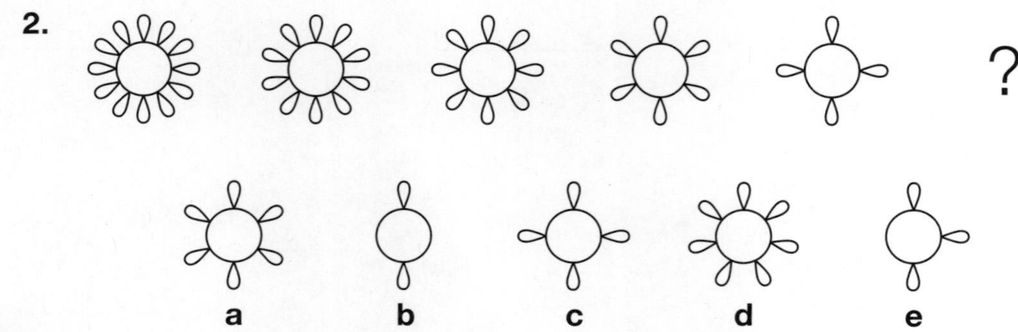

3.

      ?

a **b** **c** **d** **e**

4.

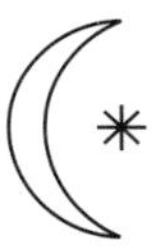     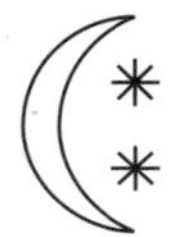 ?

a **b** **c** **d** **e**

5.

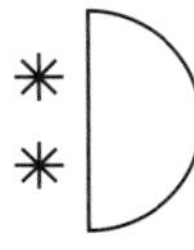  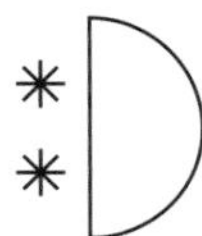  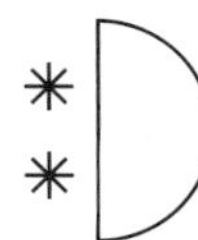  ?

a **b** **c** **d** **e**

/5

Example

Look at the shapes and patterns. Work out the code by putting the pattern and shape together. Circle the letter under the code.

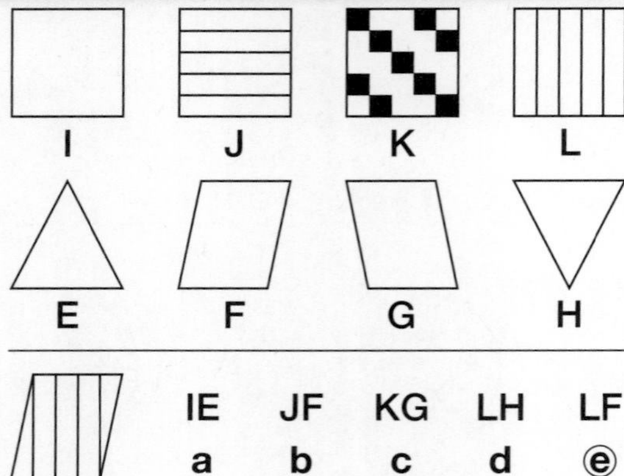

IE	JF	KG	LH	LF
a	b	c	d	ⓔ

The answer is **e** because the pattern is **L** and the shape is **F**, so the code is **LF**.

Now try these. Use the shapes and patterns below to answer the questions.

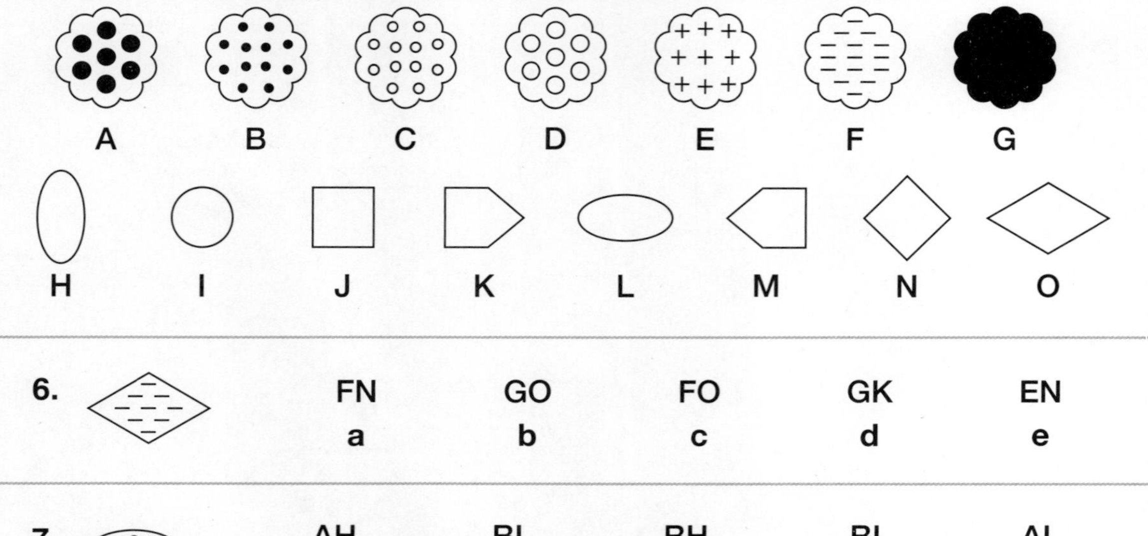

6.

FN	GO	FO	GK	EN
a	b	c	d	e

7.

AH	BL	BH	BI	AL
a	b	c	d	e

8.		DK a	CK b	CM c	DM d	DJ e
9.		GK a	FJ b	GM c	FK d	GJ e
10.		AI a	AL b	BI c	BH d	CI e

/5

Example

Which is the odd one out? Circle the letter under it.

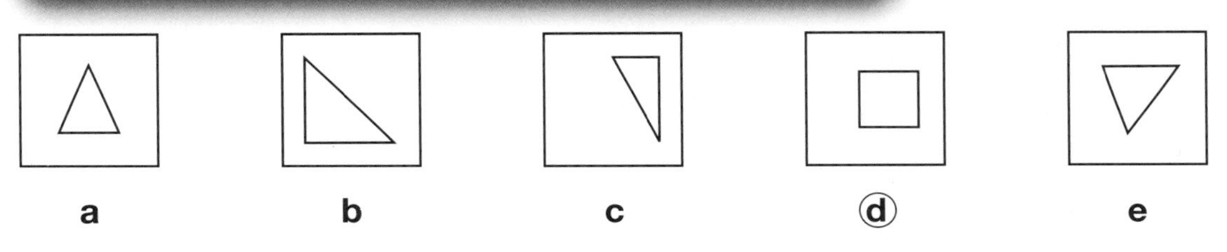

a b c ⓓ e

The answer is **d** because the shape inside the square has 4 sides. **a**, **b**, **c** and **e** are all similar because the shape inside each square has 3 sides.

Now try these. Which is the odd one out? Circle the letter under it.

11.

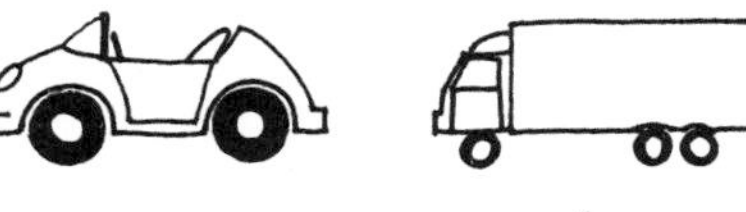

a b c d e

12.

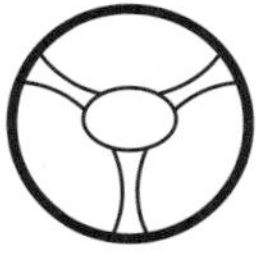

a b c d e

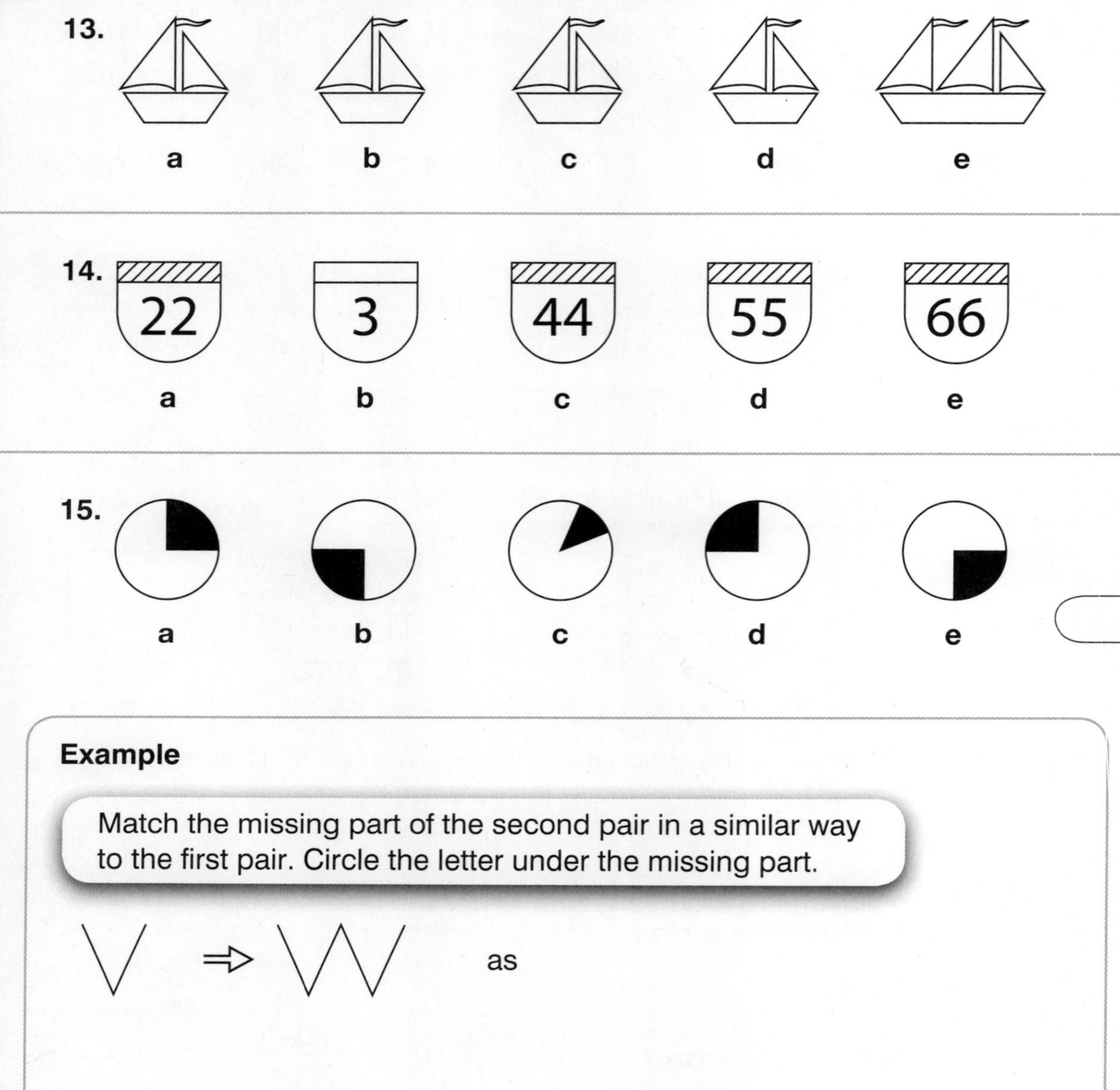

/5

Example

Match the missing part of the second pair in a similar way to the first pair. Circle the letter under the missing part.

as

a b c d ⓔ

The answer is **e** because in this example, the answer is double the first one.

Now try these. Circle the letter under the missing part.

16.  as

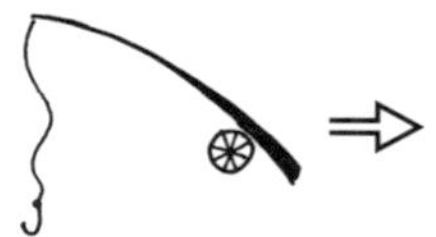

a b c d e

17.  as

 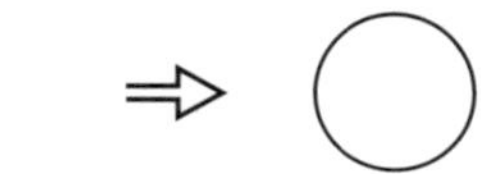

a b c d e

18.   as

 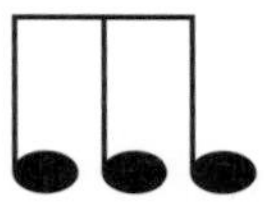  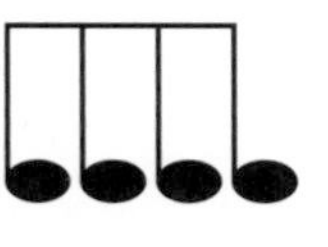

a b c d e

19.

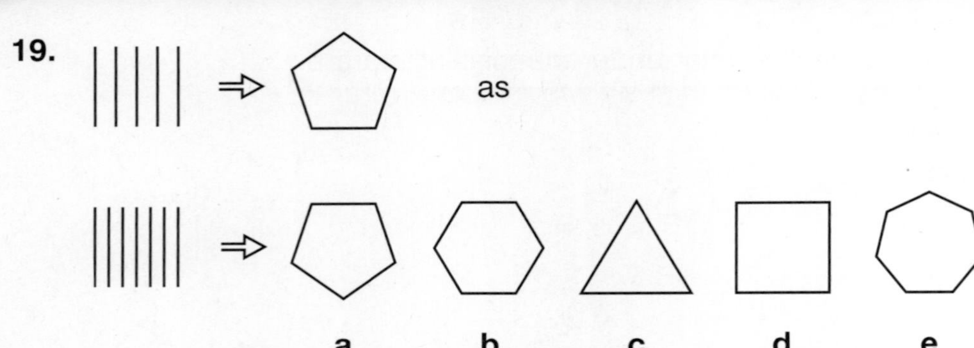

20.

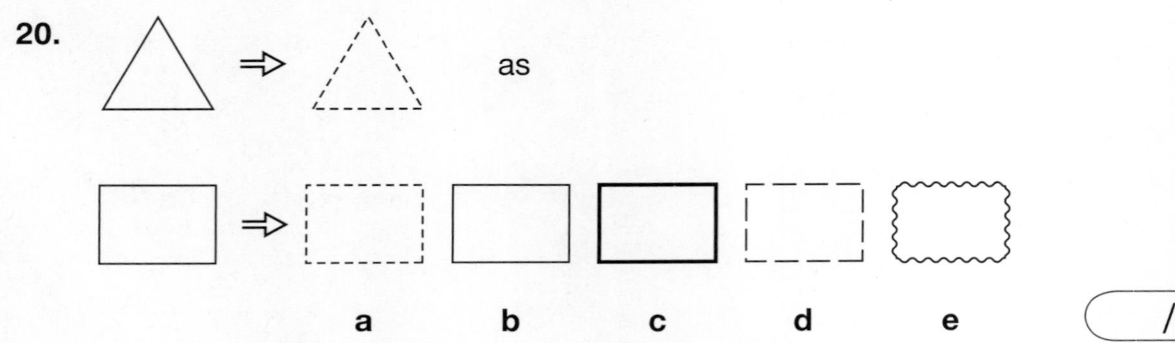

/5

Example

Complete the grid by finding the missing square.
Circle the letter under the square.

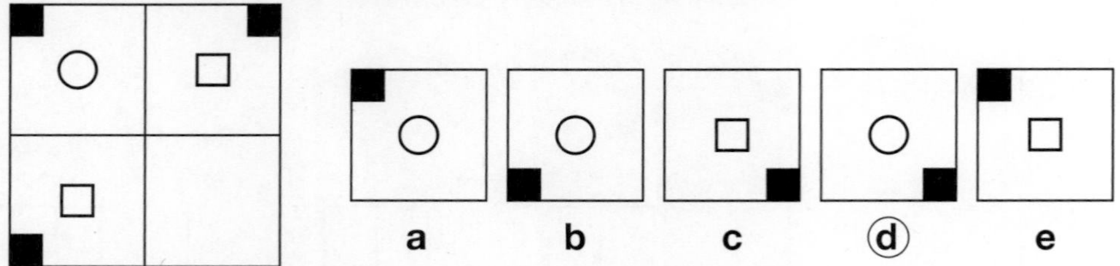

The answer is **d** because the small black squares make a pattern on the outer corners of the whole grid.

The middle of the missing part is a circle. The top of the grid is a circle and a square, so the bottom line becomes a square and then a circle.

Now try these. Circle the letter under the missing square.

21. 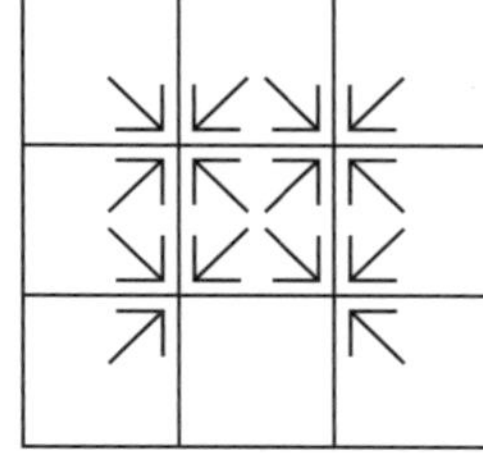

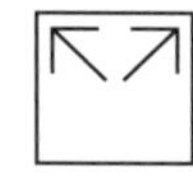 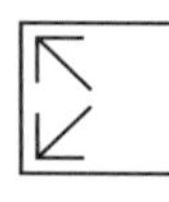  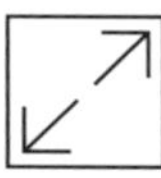 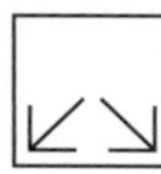

a b c d e

22. 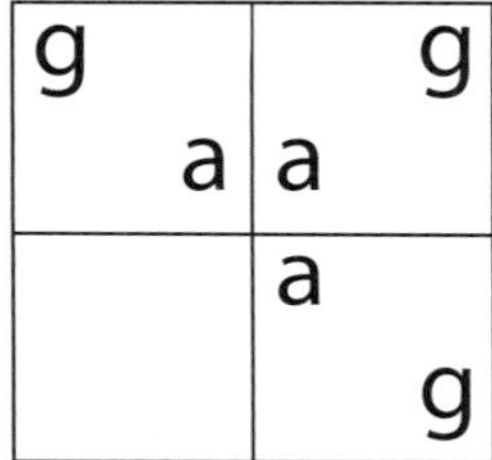

a	b	c	d	e
a g	g a	a a	a g	g g

23. 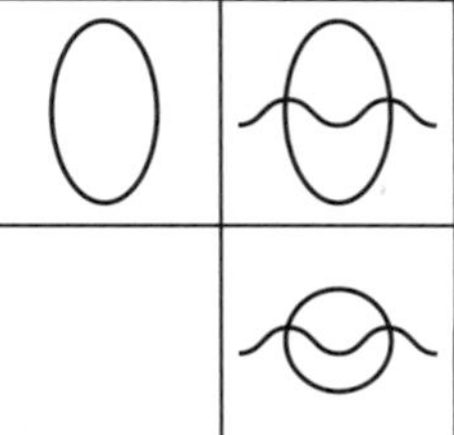

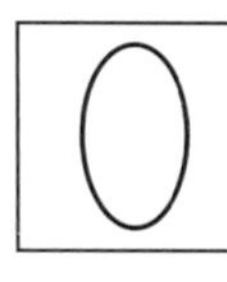 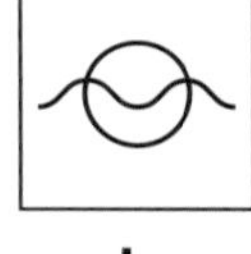 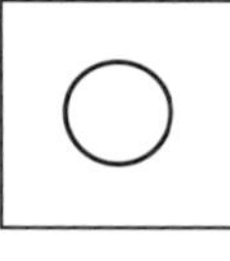 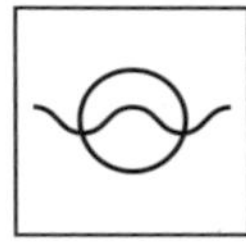 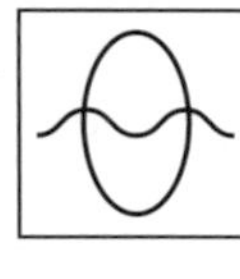

a b c d e

24. 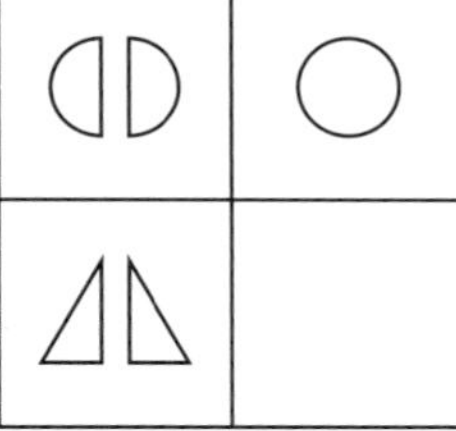

  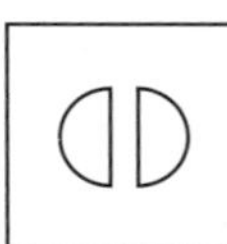 

a b c d e

25. 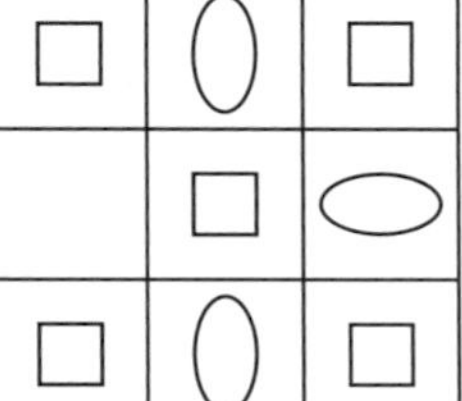

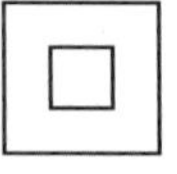  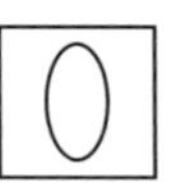 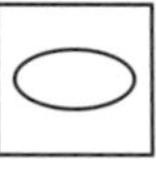

a b c d e

/5

/25

PAPER 8

Example

Which is the odd one out? Circle the letter under it.

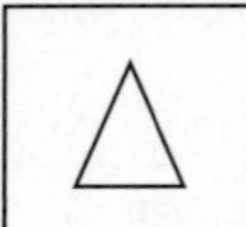 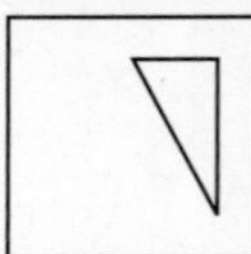 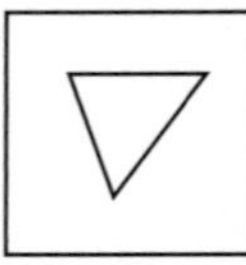

a **b** **c** **(d)** **e**

The answer is **d** because the shape inside the square has 4 sides. **a**, **b**, **c** and **e** are all similar because the shape inside each square has 3 sides.

Now try these. Which is the odd one out? Circle the letter under it.

1.

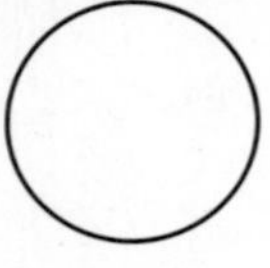    

a **b** **c** **d** **e**

2.

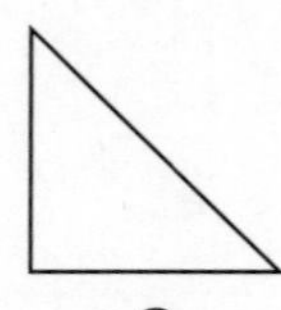 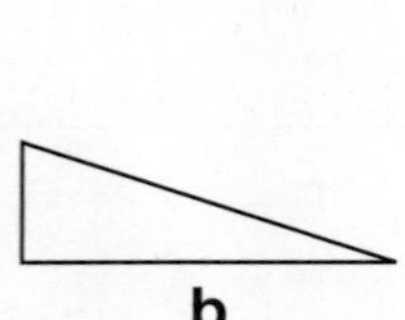   

a **b** **c** **d** **e**

3.

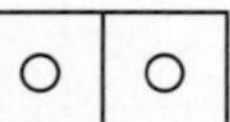 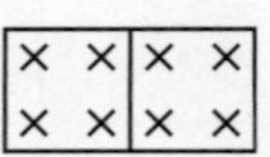 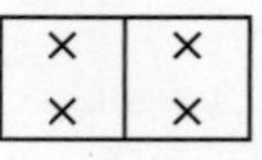 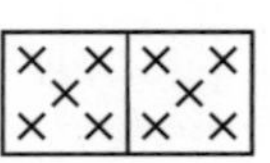 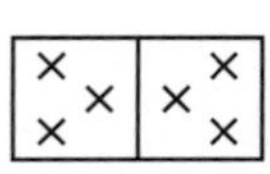

a **b** **c** **d** **e**

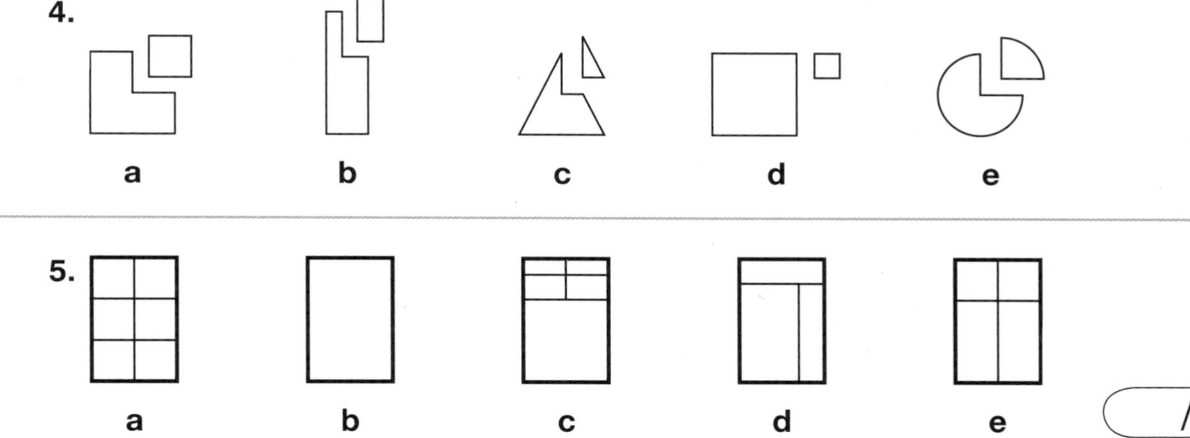

/5

Example

Match the missing part of the second pair in a similar way to the first pair. Circle the letter under the missing part.

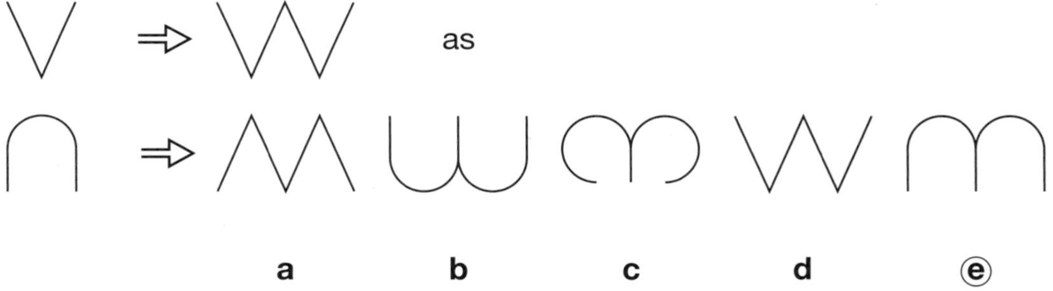

The answer is **e** because in this example, the answer is double the first one.

Now try these. Circle the letter under the missing part.

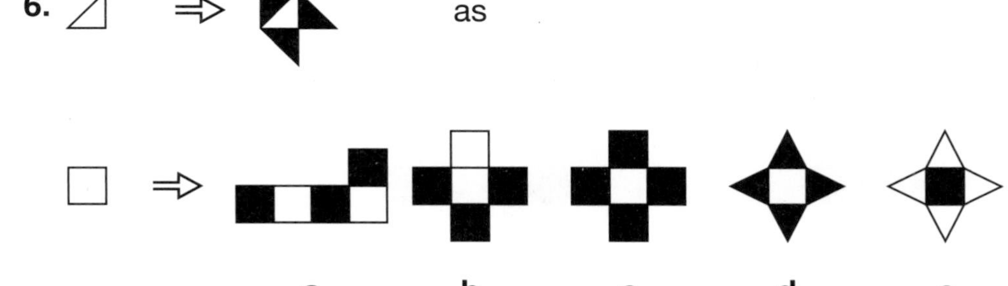

7. 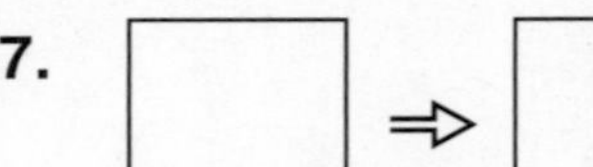 as

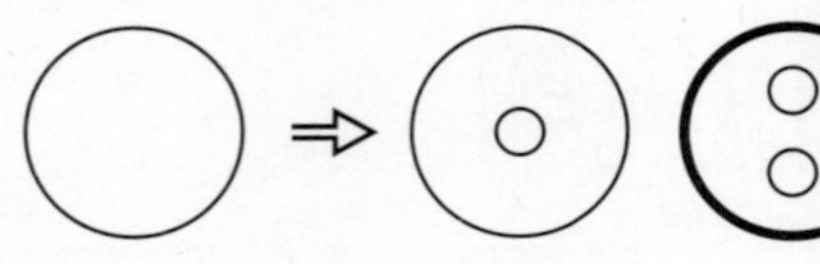 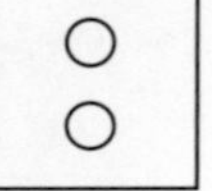 

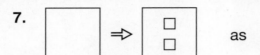

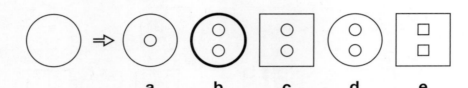

a b c d e

8. 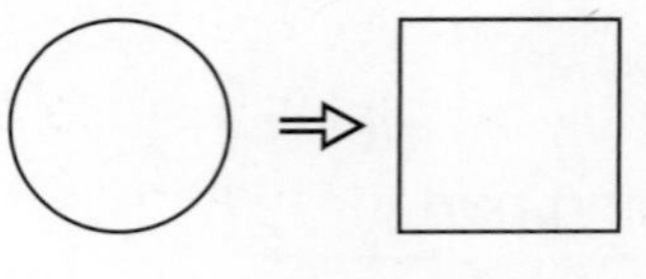 as

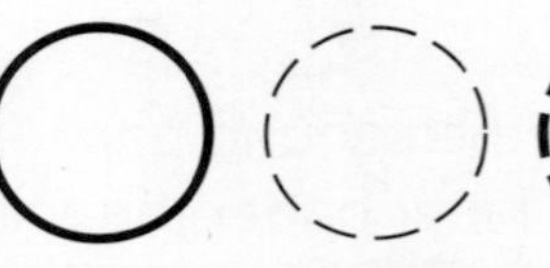 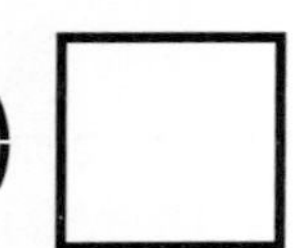

a b c d e

9.  as

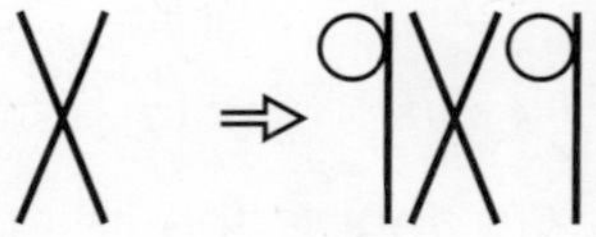  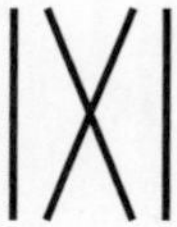 

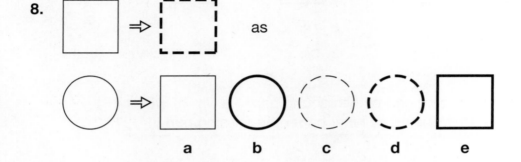

a b c d e

10. 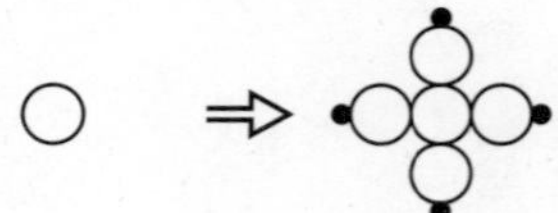 as

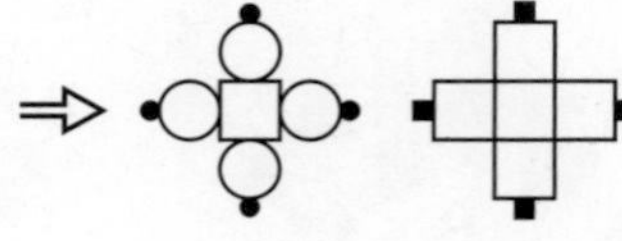 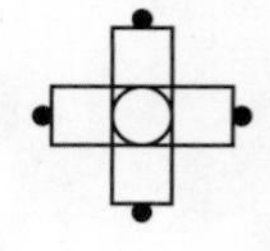 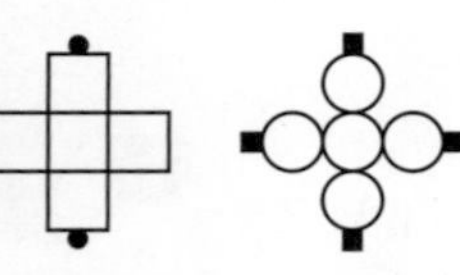 

a b c d e

/5

Example

Complete the grid by finding the missing square.
Circle the letter under the square.

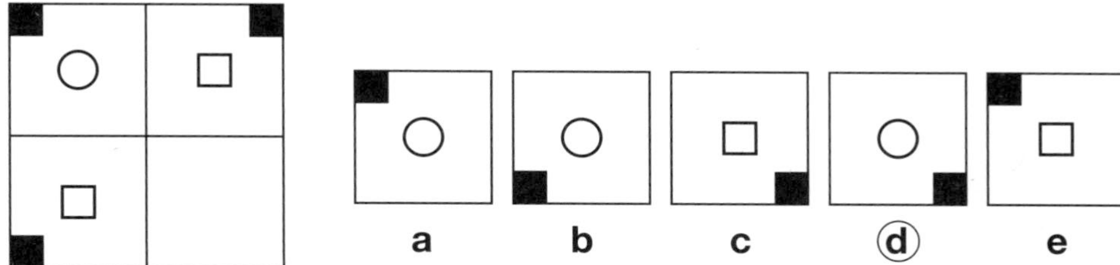

The answer is **d** because the small black squares make a pattern on the outer corners of the whole grid.

The middle of the missing part is a circle. The top of the grid is a circle and a square, so the bottom line becomes a square and then a circle.

Now try these. Circle the letter under the missing square.

11. 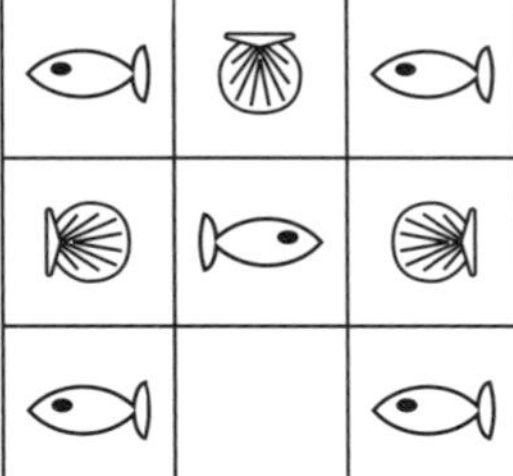

   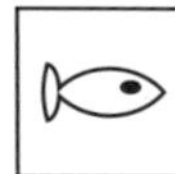 

a **b** **c** **d** **e**

12. 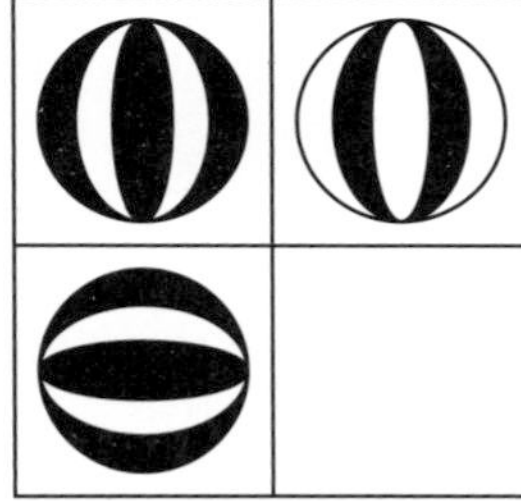

 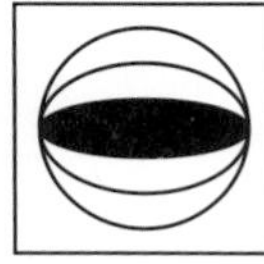 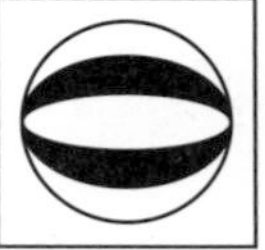  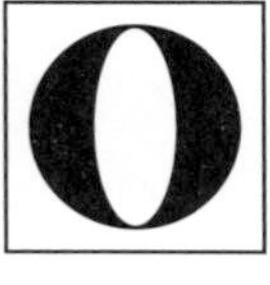

a **b** **c** **d** **e**

13.

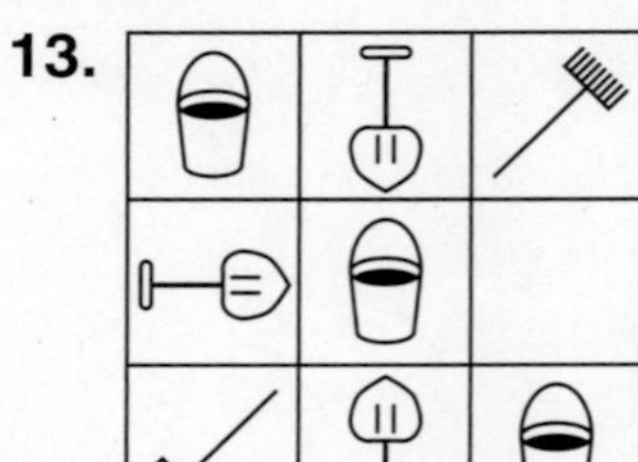

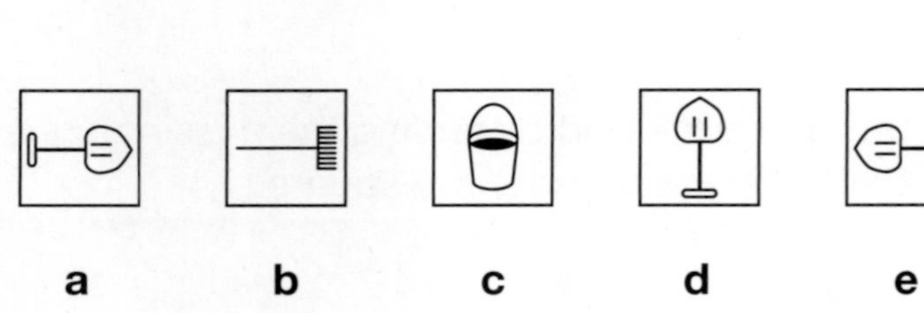

14.

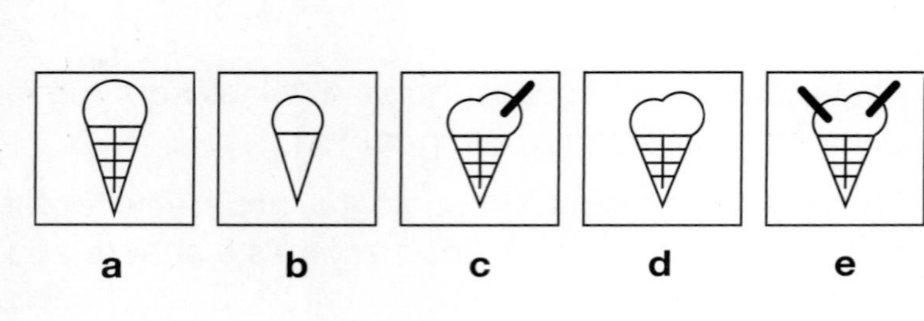

15.

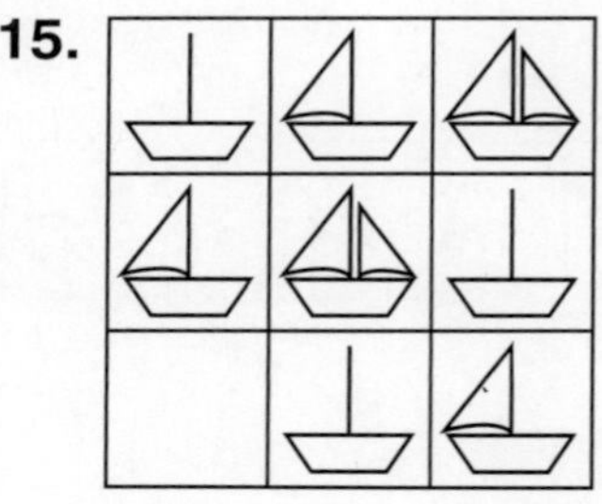

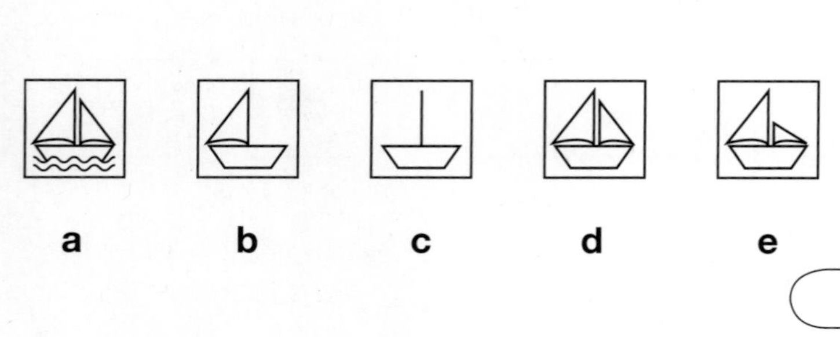

/5

Example

Look at the shapes and patterns. Work out the code by putting the pattern and shape together. Circle the letter under the code.

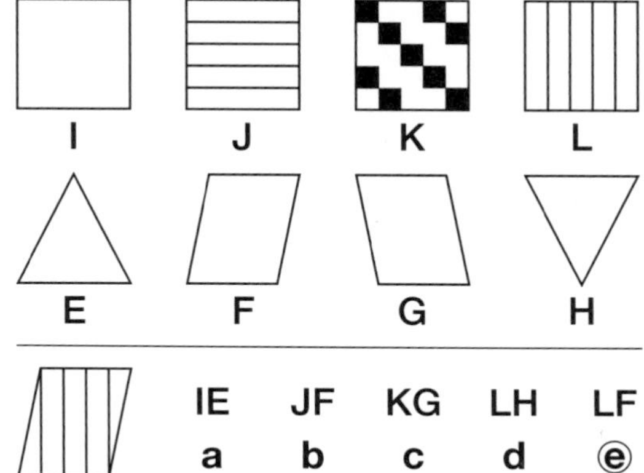

	IE	JF	KG	LH	LF
	a	b	c	d	ⓔ

The answer is **e** because the pattern is **L** and the shape is **F**, so the code is **LF**.

Now try these. Use the shapes and patterns below to answer the questions.

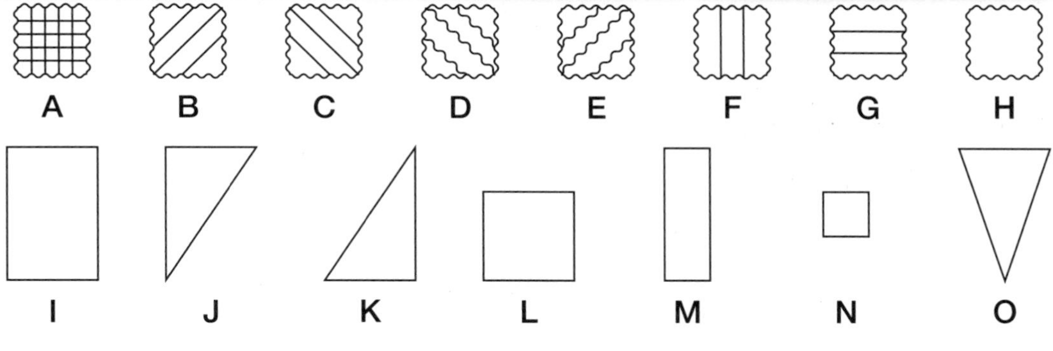

16.	CL	DM	CN	DN	GK
	a	b	c	d	e

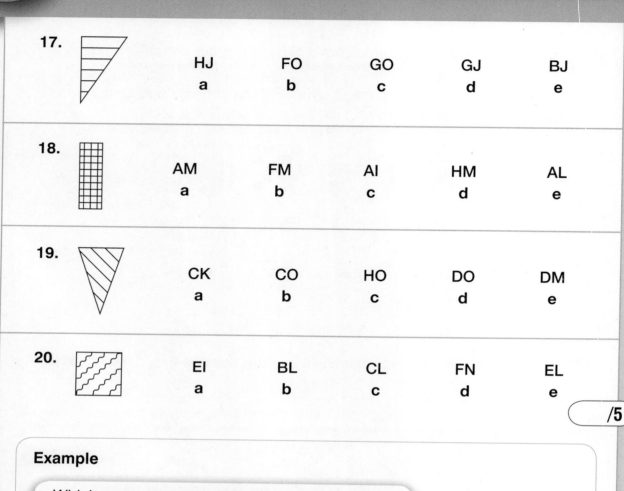

17.

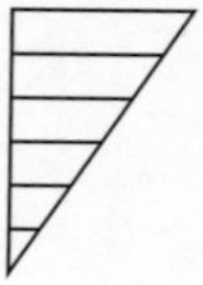

HJ	FO	GO	GJ	BJ
a	b	c	d	e

18.

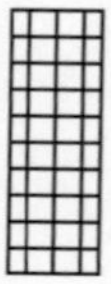

AM	FM	AI	HM	AL
a	b	c	d	e

19.

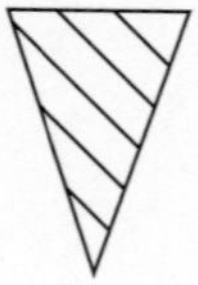

CK	CO	HO	DO	DM
a	b	c	d	e

20.

EI	BL	CL	FN	EL
a	b	c	d	e

/5

Example

Which one comes next? Circle the letter under it.

The answer is **c** because it follows the circle at the beginning of the pattern.

Now try these. Which one comes next? Circle the letter under it.

21.  ?

a b c d e

22.  ?

a b c d e

23. 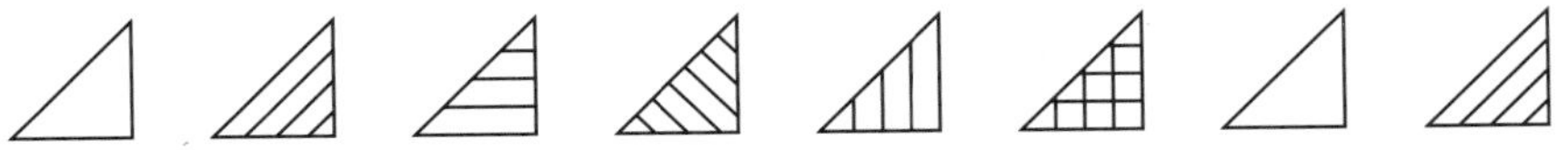 ?

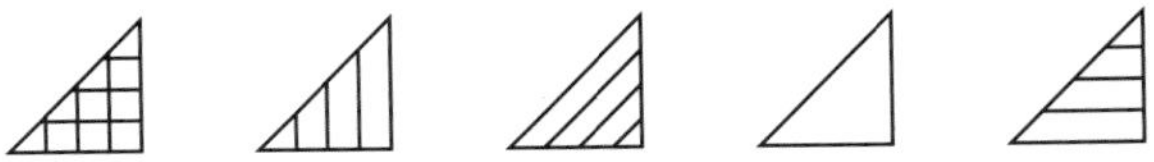

a b c d e

24. 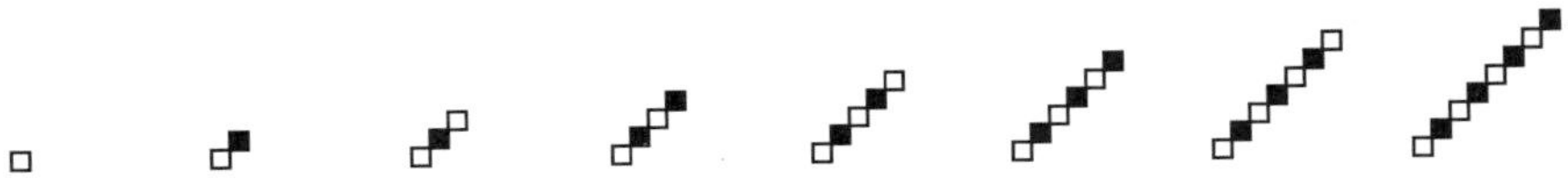 ?

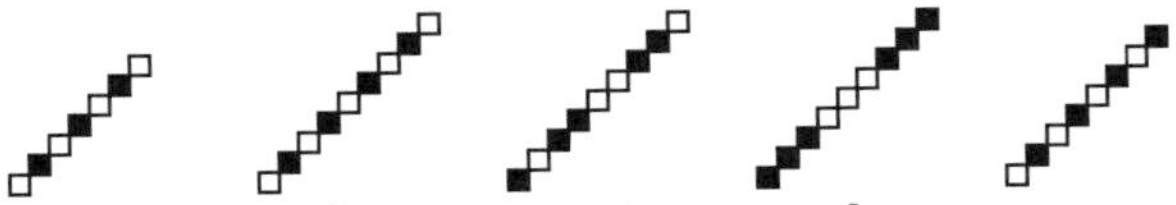

a b c d e

25. 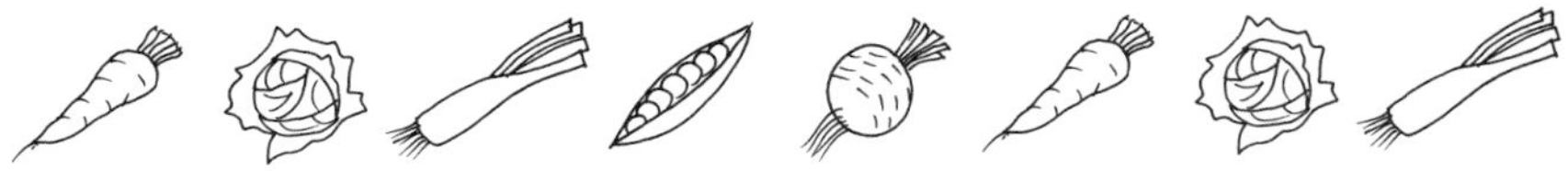 ?

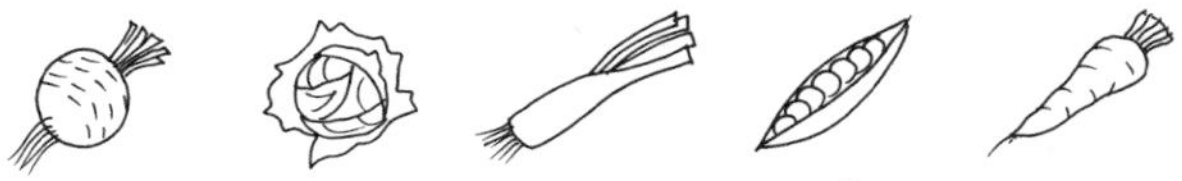

a b c d e

/5

/25

Progress grid

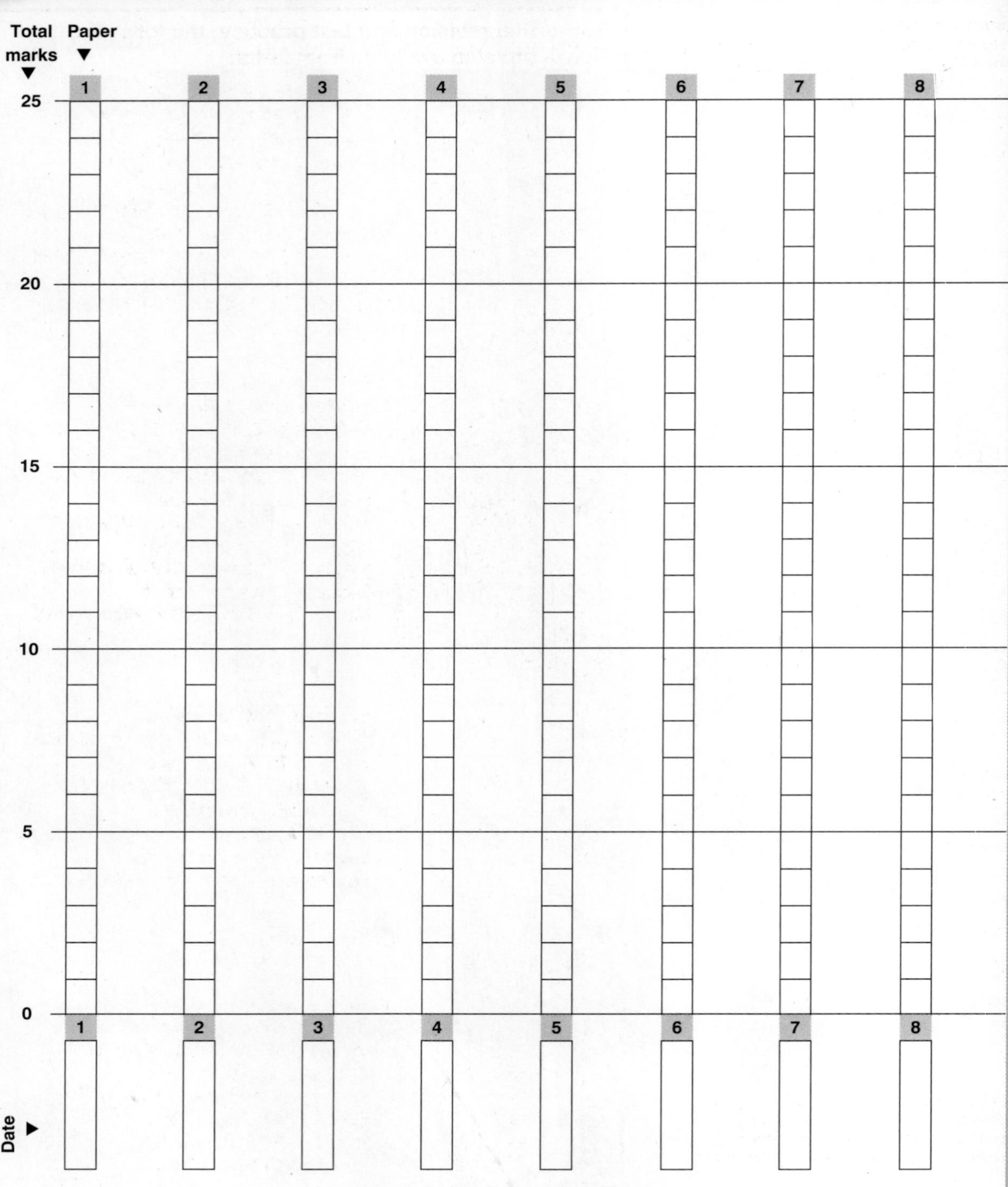

Now colour in your score!